POOLEYS

Microlight
and
Small Seaplanes

Anna Markey

Nothing in this syllabus supersedes any legislation, rules, regulations or procedures contained in any operational document issued by Her Majesty's Stationery Office, the Civil Aviation Authority, the Joint Aviation Authorities, ICAO, the manufacturers of aircraft, engines and systems, or by the operators of aircraft throughout the world.

Microlight Book and Small Seaplanes - Anna Markey

©Anna Markey 2007

ISBN 978-1-84336-139-8

Pooleys Flight Equipment Ltd
Elstree Aerodrome
Hertfordshire
WD6 3AW
England

Tel: +44(0)208 953 4870
Fax: +44(0)208 953 2512
Email: sales@pooleys.com
Website: www.pooleys.com

Acknowledgements

In writing this book, I owe a great debt of thanks to Alan Newton of On-Track Aviation who provided extensive comments and suggestions based on my original manuscript, which in turn helped make this a more complete book.

Many thanks are also due to Aimaro Malingri (Polaris Motor s.r.l.), Andy Flude, Lennart Forsmark (Fly4Fun Sweden) and Peter Wicander (Flysports Sweden) for additional comments relating to flexwing and flying boat operations and also to Bruce Ross and Terence Acton for proof-reading.

I would also like to thank the following for their various photographic contributions: Aimaro Malingri, Miguel Rosario (AirMax Brazil), Alan Newton, Andy Flude, Bruce Ross, Chip Erwin (Czech Aircraft Works), Cliff Sims, Fiona Luckhurst (Shadow Flight Centre), Jean Michel Dizier (DTA France), Lennart Forsmark, Peter Millar, Peter Wicander, Sky Ranger France, Stephen Powell (Amphibious Flying Club) and Thruster UK.

Material from the UK Hydrographic Office publications "IALA Maritime Buoyage System (NP 735)" and "Symbols and Abbreviations used on Admiralty Charts (Chart 5011)" has been used with the kind permission of the UKHO.

Material from the IMO publication "COLREG (Consolidated Edition, 2003)" is used by kind permission of the International Maritime Organization (IMO).

Photographic materials derived from Para-tech Engineering Company and B.Leglatin of Plastimo France have also been used with their permission.

Anna Markey

Anna Markey started her flying career on paragliders in the Wessex hills, before taking to powered flight on flexwing microlights at Old Sarum airfield. In parallel with pursuing an international career as a financial and IT consultant, she moved on to 3-axis microlights, a JAR PPL and light aircraft seaplane rating. Subsequently she became a microlight instructor and took a well-timed career break, seizing an opportunity to instruct on seaplane microlights in Sweden - 'the best seaplane environment in Europe'. Since then, Anna has become a BMAA examiner and now offers the microlight seaplane rating to UK pilots from her Swedish lake-land base at Siljan Airpark. This book evolved out of a need to bridge the gap in training material between light aircraft and smaller seaplanes. Anna uses the amphibious Seamax 3-axis flying boat and Polaris am-FIB flexwing for training.

Photo: Anna with her Seamax training aircraft in Sweden

Table of Contents

- Acknowledgements

- Introduction

- **Chapter 1** - Seaplane types, components & pre-flight inspection

- **Chapter 2** - Taxying and manoeuvring on the water

- **Chapter 3** - Taking off

- **Chapter 4** - Landing and approaching the dock

- **Chapter 5** - Mooring and securing the seaplane

- **Chapter 6** - Emergency procedures; capsize and recovery

- **Chapter 7** - Obtaining a seaplane rating: training and theory

Appendices:

Appendix A: Beaufort Scale
Appendix B: Knots
Appendix C: Bibliography and Further Reading

Introduction

Introduction to Microlight and Small Seaplanes

Photo: DTA Floatplane Prototype, south of France   Photo: Seamax Flying Boat, Stockholm archipelago

The primary intention of this book is to assist the novice seaplane pilot in understanding the techniques and acquiring the knowledge to attain his sea rating in a microlight or small seaplane. In doing so, it is not intended to be a substitute for proper instruction gained with an experienced seaplane instructor. Rather, it is intended as a supplement to such instruction and may be regarded as study material prior to attending a seaplane course. If a prospective seaplane pilot has fully read and digested the material contained herein, it will make both his task - and that of the instructor - so much easier during the course itself.

There is much to explain with regard to seaplane flying and this book grew out of the need to produce 'long briefings' to microlight seaplane students, where such existing material was either difficult to obtain or more geared towards larger, light aircraft seaplanes such as Cessna floatplanes. To my knowledge, no book to date has been written specifically for small seaplanes and this book therefore aims to fill that gap. The light aircraft seaplane pilot may also find much of technical interest in this book, since many of the techniques and characteristics discussed are equally relevant to all seaplanes. However, there are differences between flying high-inertia and low-inertia aircraft, as well as differences between particular types and this book is definitely not 'type specific'. It is crucial to thoroughly read the Pilots' Operating Handbook (POH) for the specific aircraft one intends to fly and refer to the manufacturer for any clarification/omissions.

Readers of this book should be aware that the range of techniques covered is primarily those basic techniques which are required to obtain a sea rating. It also includes some areas which are considered 'advanced' seaplane flying, such as operating on currents and takeoff from restricted areas. However it should be borne in mind that ANY seaplane flying - even that considered within the 'basic' category - is more fraught with dangers and less forgiving of error than normal land plane flying. In this sense, ALL seaplane flying is 'advanced flying' and as such should be treated with due caution and respect.

Not only does this book deal with the practical techniques associated with flying seaplanes, it also gives an outline of the requirements for the seamanship exam from a theoretical point of view. Therefore the subjects of Buoys and Buoyage, Collision Regulations, Tides and other subjects relevant to the theoretical exam are included.

This book is written as a generic guide to flying microlight seaplanes and other small seaplanes. The main body of each chapter covers techniques which are relevant to 3-axis types as well as in principle to flexwing types. Major differences relating to flexwing aircraft are discussed in separate sections entitled 'Flexwing Considerations', which follow the main body of each chapter. Therefore the flexwing pilot should read the main body of each chapter in addition to the 'Flexwing Considerations' sections. It is assumed that the reader is already aware of how to fly a low-inertia aeroplane and of the control differences between 3-axis and flexwing aircraft.

With regard to obtaining a rating, one important question that might arise is 'what is the point?' since at the time of writing there are very few UK-certified microlight seaplanes (mainly due to weight restrictions) and few seaplanes of any type in the UK (although their number is growing). The answer to this is multi-faceted. Part of the answer relies on the fact that more and more microlight and small aircraft manufacturers are looking to provide floats as an option on their aircraft and that given sufficient time and interest such options will be available within the permitted weight range.

It is also necessary to have somewhere to fly the seaplane. Scotland and Northern Ireland are better endowed than England and Wales with inland waterways, and more disposed to grant the necessary permissions to make use of them. However there are several bodies of water in England and Wales that could be used by seaplanes and simply require that one makes the necessary enquiries to obtain permission. The whole of the UK also has a significant area of coast line. Sea water is somewhat less seaplane-friendly than inland waterways and poses a bigger problem with corrosion but is by no means unusable. All of these potential 'hydrodromes' require that permission be sought from the relevant land owners, local authorities or port authorities. It will be up to pilots who want to fly seaplanes in their local area to foster a relationship with their local water authority to gain access to some of these waterways. That is something that will take time to negotiate but should become more commonplace given sufficient enthusiasm from the right kind of knowledgeable and responsible pilots. Equally, with travel to Europe becoming increasingly common, there are many opportunities for flying seaplanes overseas.

And so to the point: which is simply that seaplane flying is one of the most fun forms of aviation invented. Seaplanes and microlights are natural allies: when a light aircraft seaplane pilot waxes lyrical about the joys of seaplane flying it is often the aspect of freedom from controlled airspace and the restrictions of the circuit that are the points most emphasised. These freedoms have long been the privilege of microlight pilots, for whilst many operate from controlled airfields, they still have the freedom to land at 'unimproved' sites and farmers' fields (with the necessary permission). Adding floats to the equation means taking this freedom a stage further by allowing the opportunity to land and take off on water, a simply exhilarating experience which once tried never fails to leave one wanting more. Water flying is fun, complex and challenging, a combination which should appeal to any pilot wanting to add an exciting new dimension to their flying skills.

Photo: Piper Cub on floats, Loch Earn, Scotland.
One of the lighter-weight floatplanes in the 'light aircraft' category, this is a 2-seater tandem floatplane.

$$\mathcal{C}hapter\ 1$$

Seaplane Types, Components and Pre-flight Inspection

Photo: Seamax 3-axis amphibious flying boat (wheels retracted)

Types

Many variations of seaplane have existed in the past, but we can classify modern day examples into two main types:

Type 1: Hull - where the aircraft fuselage takes the shape of a boat and
Type 2: Float - where two hydrodynamic floats are fitted to an existing land-plane.

The former are known as 'flying boats' and the latter as 'floatplanes'. The term 'seaplane' is a generic word covering both types.

As a general rule, flying boats are designed with the kind of robust, boat-like fuselages that you would expect from any vessel designed for use on the open water. Floatplanes, on the other hand, are exactly the same aircraft as the land-plane they originate from, but with the addition of two floats. Whilst designed to be sea-worthy, these floats are generally speaking slightly less robust than a flying boat hull and more vulnerable to large waves and rough seas. Floats without wheels are called 'straight floats' as opposed to wheeled, amphibious floats. The photos below show a land-plane version of the Skyranger microlight and its float-plane equivalent.

Skyranger - wheel plane version   Skyranger with 'straight' floats

The control systems for either a flying boat or a floatplane may be the more usual 3-axis type (stick/yoke and rudder) or the flexwing type, controlled by weightshift. In the photos below we can see both types of seaplane with weightshift controls:

Flexwing flying boat (Polaris FIB), Sweden   Flexwing floatplane (Mainair Sprint on floats), Thailand

The behavioural characteristics of a microlight or small seaplane on water are similar to those of any larger seaplane, except that being smaller and lighter they have the handling differences associated with lower inertia aircraft. In the case of flexwing aircraft, there is no 'light aircraft' equivalent: they are always 'microlights'.

It should be noted that there can be considerable differences between the handling and flying characteristics of flying boats and floatplanes, with the engine position also making a significant contribution to handling considerations. As a general rule, what follows can be considered applicable to all seaplane types, but where key differences exist between the two types (floatplanes and flying boats) an attempt is made to point this out. Key differences between 3-axis and flexwing handling are given separately under 'Flexwing Considerations' at the end of each section. Finally it must be noted that due to the many varieties of small seaplane available that it is always necessary to consult the Pilot's Operating Handbook (POH) or refer to the manufacturer in question for the characteristics of any specific type.

Components

Whether the aircraft is equipped with dual floats or a boat-shaped mono-hull, the design and function of the under-surface is subject to the same principles.

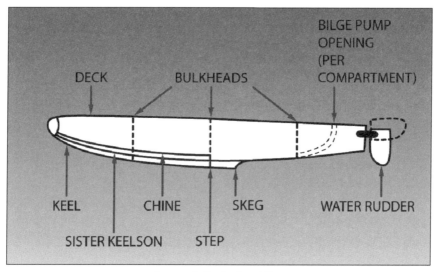

Diagram: Profile of a Typical Float

Floats and Hulls

Floats may be constructed of aluminium, rubber or composite materials. Damage can occur to any kind of float and the 'best' material to use is subject to debate. Small holes and punctures in most types of material can be repaired quite easily providing the aircraft is removed from the water. Whilst it may be good practice to carry a small repair kit in the cockpit for emergencies, damage occurring below the waterline is very difficult to repair whilst on the water itself. In the case of metal and composite floats it is best to seek a specialist to repair the damage. Be aware that small amounts of water in the float compartments do not necessarily mean there is a puncture. Most floats leak a little through the unavoidable joins and rivets, though well-made floats in good repair should only do so when subjected to high water pressure on take-off, landing and fast taxiing. (Note that it is exactly during these phases of operation that a float may fill with water after having gained a small puncture which went unnoticed during idle taxi on the water).

Float Buoyancy

The floats or hull of a seaplane have to support the weight of the aircraft whilst it is at rest or moving slowly on the water. They do this by displacing an amount of water which is equal in weight to that of the aircraft. This means that the more weight you add to the aircraft, the lower the floats will sink in the water, since they have to displace more water to support the additional weight.

When referring to floats, the manufacturer will ascribe a buoyancy figure to them, which is a measure of the displacement of weight of fresh water per float (fresh water being less buoyant than salt water). This measure has traditionally been in pounds (lbs) - according to American convention - so, for example, a float which is designated a '1400' will displace 1400lb of aircraft weight. To know how much buoyancy you actually need, note that according to the United States Federal Aviation Regulations (FAR) part 23, section 23.753 states that each float must have 'a buoyancy of 80% in excess of the buoyancy required by that float to support its portion of the maximum weight of the seaplane or amphibian in fresh water'. This US rule is quoted since there is no equivalent law in the UK ANO. What the rule means in plain language is that each float must support 80% of the aircraft weight, so an aircraft weighing, for example, 900lb must be fitted with floats which could support at least 720lb each. Note that when dealing with floats manufactured outside the US the buoyancy figure could be in lbs or kg.

Hydrodynamic Force

Supporting the aircraft at idle in the water is one thing, but when it comes to increasing speed in order to take off, the floats/hull have to push a large amount of water ahead of them. The hydrodynamic drag thus encountered, which increases as the square of the groundspeed, has to be overcome by the specially designed under-surface. The forward section of the under-surface deflects water and air downwards and sidewards, creating hydrodynamic lift as an equal and opposite force, rather like a speedboat.

The rear section is carefully designed to allow the aircraft to break away from the water surface adhesion and become airborne. It achieves this by the break in the under-surface known as the 'Step' which allows it to pitch forwards to minimise the amount of water contact and hence reduce friction, allowing speed on the water to build until flying speed is attained. The Step is situated close to the Centre of Gravity (CG).

To explain how this works in more detail, applying full power and maintaining a positive angle of attack in relation to the water flow (stick fully back) will allow the bow of the float/hull to rise out of the water, reducing contact with the water and therefore reducing hydrodynamic drag. This causes a wave of water to build up in front of the floats/hull and the pilot will see the nose rise. Depending on the aircraft, there may be one or two stages of nose rise as the floats climb higher on the wave. As the top of the wave is reached the centre of balance moves aft, observed by the spray pattern moving rearward from the bows to just forward of the Step. With (normally) just a little relaxing of pressure on the stick (type depending) the aircraft will transition to a flatter planing attitude, supported by the hydrodynamic force on a small area of the under-surface just forward of the step. This area is known as the 'sweet spot' and maintaining this spot is necessary to continue a high speed taxy.

As ground-speed increases in this attitude, the hydrodynamic tendency of the floats takes over from their buoyancy in supporting the aircraft.

As well as the hydrodynamic lift force, the wings will also start to develop lift as the groundspeed increases and take off can be achieved once the lift from the wings is equal to the weight of the seaplane. The stern of the float/hull is shaped upwards towards the rear, allowing the aircraft to pitch up for take off.

The inclusion of the step, which allows the necessary breakpoint, unfortunately has a drawback: it creates a stress point on the underside and causes considerable drag in flight. So while the step is absolutely necessary, it must be designed to be as small as possible while still capable of fulfilling its function.

Photo: this picture of a Polaris FIB (amphibious version) in flight clearly shows the step section which in this version comprises several cut-away sections from mid-point to abaft the rubber boat.

9

Other Features

Other note-worthy features of the float construction include the Bulkheads, Keel, Skeg and Chines. The bulkheads separate the float into different watertight compartments, so that if one compartment is holed or leaking the entire float will not fill up with water. Equally, the compartments serve to keep any ingressed water in one small area, and not sloshing around the entire length of the float, which could seriously affect the aircraft CG at a critical time.

However rocks or other solid obstructions in the water could hole more than one compartment at a time. The ingress of water may not be noticeable at first, but a subsequent high-speed taxi may well cause the compartment(s) to fill up due to the increased water pressure. At least four compartments per float are normal, but many light aircraft floats have more than this. The compartment walls provide extra rigidity and strengthen the floats however they also add more weight - always an adverse consideration when dealing with microlights.

Whilst the diagram above shows many of the possible features on a float, some of these may be adapted on microlight floats because of weight restrictions. Sometimes, microlight floatplanes are equipped with floats adapted from the light aircraft world (e.g. EDO or Full Lotus floats) whilst other manufacturers will prefer to make their own, more suited to the weight restrictions of the smaller aircraft world. There are also some floats especially made for microlight operations, e.g. Czech floats make special microlight versions. Be careful: it should go without saying, but good floats are essential to a seaplane, so make sure that the floats chosen are suitably robust and not just a compromise to save weight.

Photo: Czech floats

The Keel is a strip running underneath the float or hull, from the centre of the bow to the step. At the step is a short section called the Skeg which, like a small underwater fin, assists with directional control. The Chines run longitudinally along the float where the side and bottom of the float meet. They allow for riveting or joining of the float surfaces and may be a suitable attachment point for spray rails (if fitted). Spray Rails serve to reduce the amount of spray contacting the propeller at high speed, which can do immense damage.

Another feature on some floats is the addition of two 'Sister Keelsons' which run parallel to the keel, aft of the bow and forward of the step. These are hydrodynamic lift boosters, which assist in reducing the time taken for a float to reach planing speed by forcing the water back towards the step. At high speed they also increase directional control on the water. These features may be found in modified format on microlight seaplanes. See the photo below.

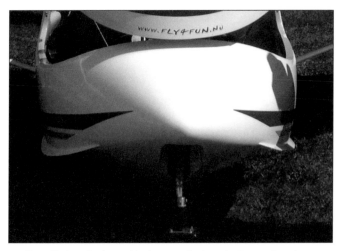

Photo: Keel, partly obscured by the nose wheel, on this Seamax flying boat.
The Chines and Sister Keelsons are also visible.

All seaplanes have at least one, and often two water rudders. Whilst two is normal with larger seaplanes, as usual with microlights, weight is an issue. Whether one or two, they are attached to the air rudders by cables and pulleys, so that when the water rudder is in the 'down' position, operating the rudder pedals also activates the water rudders.

Most seaplanes have springs in the lines to/from the water rudder and air rudder so that should one or other of the water rudders jam then the air rudder is not restricted causing problems in directional control.

There is a mechanism in the cockpit to lower and retract the water rudders as necessary. The pre-flight inspection should pay particular attention to the mechanisms which operate the water rudder, since without this there may be very little directional control on the water.

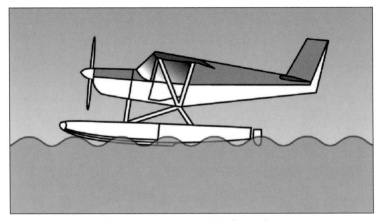

Floatplane profile showing typical water rudder, float and strut arrangement

In the case of a floatplane, the aircraft itself must be securely fastened to the floats. This is normally done by the use of additional struts, commonly three such struts: forward, diagonal and aft, although sometimes there are only forward and aft struts. Spreader bars are attached between each float as an additional measure to decrease the effect of a hard landing and protect the attachment points of the strut to the float. Finally, bracing wires attached in a crossed pair below the fuselage provide added rigidity to the float arrangement. See diagram above for a typical configuration and photograph below for a real life version.

Photo: one particular configuration of struts with bracing wires
positioned diagonally at the float attachment points

One feature specific to flying boat types is that they often have sponsons or wingtip floats to increase the roll stability of the aircraft on the water. These will be attached to the fuselage or the under-surface of the wing, slightly inboard of the tips.

Photo: Seamax with sponsons just inboard of wing tips. Barkarby Airfield, Stockholm

Additionally, flying boats which have the engine mounted aloft (see photo of Seamax above) often have 'vortex generators' attached to the fuselage in such a position that they create a smoother flow of air behind the trailing edge of the wing into the path of the propeller.

Photo: vortex generators

Both flying boats and floatplanes may or may not have wheels fitted. Floats without wheels are known as 'straight floats' (nothing to do with the shape). Seaplanes with wheels are known as 'amphibious'. Being equipped with wheels allows the obvious advantage of being able to land on land as well as water. Amphibious floats normally have a small wheel at the tip of each float (or sometimes one central front wheel) to assist taxying on land. In the case of amphibians, it is vitally important to adhere strictly to a pre-landing checklist to ensure that the wheels are correctly selected up or down, depending on whether one is landing on water or land.

Photos: 3 types of microlight seaplane converted to amphibian

1. Amphibious Storch
2. Amphibious Mainair Sprint
3. Polaris 'Am-FIB' Flying Boat

With the major advantage conferred by having wheels, one might ask why anyone would opt for a non-amphibious seaplane. There are three main considerations. Firstly, microlights in particular are subject to strict weight restrictions. The maximum take off weight for a microlight is 450 kg plus a further 45 kg (in the UK) for a seaplane (whether flying boat or floatplane). Unfortunately it is difficult to find a set of amphibious floats weighing less than 45 kg, so if the microlight in question is already at the top end of the weight range then the addition of wheels might take it over the limit. The second consideration is complexity. Wheels require an extra mechanism to extend and retract them, adding further to the weight and introducing the possibility of mechanical failure. The third main consideration concerns the fact that although the landing possibilities are greatly increased, so are the opportunities for making a serious error, in that inadvertently landing with wheels down on water could cause a grave accident. It is It is possible in such a case for the aircraft to tip over, with potentially fatal consequences. Interestingly, landing a seaplane wheels up on land is generally less of a problem: landing wheels up on grass generally causes no damage and can be more desirable in the event of an engine failure over 'unprepared' land than landing wheels down. Inadvertently landing wheels up on tarmac - whilst undesirable - may cause nothing more than repairable damage (and a red face).

Pre-flight Inspection

The pre-flight inspection should include all the normal elements relevant to a landplane plus those additional elements relevant to a seaplane. Any peculiarities of type should be specified in the POH. If the aircraft is in water during the pre-flight inspection take a look at the entire plane from a short distance away: just as when an aircraft stands on land, it should be possible to see if there is something 'not quite symmetrical' which in this instance may indicate water in one or more float compartments causing the seaplane to lean slightly to one side.

If the aircraft is amphibious and positioned on land or a ramp then the walk-around is fairly straightforward. However, amphibious floatplanes can stand quite tall (with the addition of both floats and wheels) so there may be some parts which can only be inspected properly with the assistance of a stepladder. Make sure you keep some suitable steps handy, so that you are not tempted to cut corners with the inspection. Otherwise you may need to develop a good climbing technique. Note also that the additional height and hence higher centre of gravity (CG) on many amphibious floatplanes makes them a little more susceptible to strong winds while on the ground, so keep a good eye or ideally two tethers on them when the aircraft is outdoors in gusty conditions.

If in water, it may be necessary to rotate the aircraft 360 degrees so that all parts of the aircraft can be carefully inspected. After the overall view, first one side of the aircraft must be inspected and the aircraft turned carefully to inspect the front, rear and other side. It may be advisable to obtain the assistance of a third party to turn the aircraft in order to avoid damage at the mooring, especially if there is any wind. An aircraft on water is a moving affair and one should never be too proud to ask for help. But always ensure that the help is well briefed and understands what to do. Keep instructions short, clear and simple - or damage may occur. In particular, always warn a helper to keep clear of the propeller end.

It is important of course to pay particular attention to the floats or hull. The float compartments must be opened and inspected and any water removed using a bilge pump. Care must be taken to replace the bilge covers and secure them properly afterwards. Inspect each compartment in turn and replace the cover immediately. Water carried in the compartments would add considerably to the weight of the aircraft and could adversely affect the CofG and take-off performance. The bilge pump must be carried in the cockpit during each flight in case of any in-flight leakage. In the case of a flying boat hull there are no compartments to inspect but look for any signs of leakage in the cockpit. There is often an electric bilge pump fitted in these types to remove any water that leaks or infiltrates the cockpit, e.g. through the canopy vents and seals.

All attachments between the floats and the fuselage should be carefully checked for any damage, corrosion or cracks. The same goes for the spreader bars and bracing wires and their attachments. The bracing wires themselves should be completely taut. Examine the cables, pulleys and attachments to the water rudders with particular care. Failure of the water rudder would mean a complete lack of directional control on the water at low speeds.

Unless submerged in water, check the area around the step and skeg with extreme care since these areas are subject to considerable stress. When the aircraft is planing it is doing so from just aft to just forward of this area. If the aircraft is in the water during the pre-flight inspection it may be difficult to perform this check adequately. In the case of an amphibian, the opportunity should be taken when the aircraft is on land for a more thorough inspection.

Another area that 'takes a pounding' - quite literally - during water operations is the propeller. Water spray is terribly damaging, such that on some types a propeller blade can be completely destroyed by clumsy piloting in a very short time. This is usually where the propeller is close to the water and the aircraft prone to create spray, such as some flexwing types where the engine is rear mounted. Small areas of damage may be dressed down and repaired, but larger areas need professional attention. Note that small areas can grow into large areas very quickly, since a pre-damaged area will deteriorate exponentially. So always inspect the propeller carefully and make repairs as soon as any damage is found.

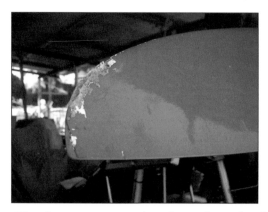

Photo: Water damage to a rear-mounted propeller on a flexwing flying boat

The same water spray that adversely affects the propeller can cause damage to the vulnerable tail end of the aircraft. The air rudder, elevator, trim tabs and any hinges and fittings can all suffer cumulative damage through regular high velocity water sprayings.

Having completed the pre-flight checks in terms of fuselage and structure, make sure that the cockpit interior is tidy, safety equipment is in place and readily accessible and loose objects are tidied away. For some reason, a seaplane tends to attract more clutter and debris than a landplane - maybe something to do with being a hybrid boat. Not only does this add weight and look messy, it can detract from the ability to find a safety device quickly in an emergency. Somebody once commented that 'safety equipment on-hand is emergency gear; everything else is camping gear'. In other words, if you can't put your hand immediately on that valuable piece of emergency equipment you know you stashed somewhere, you might as well not have it.

The UK ANO Schedule 4 Article 19 (9) and 19 (2) lists mandatory equipment as follows:

- One life jacket or equivalent floatation device for each person on board stowed in a position readily accessible from his seat
- Equipment for making the sound signals prescribed in the International Regulations for Preventing Collisions at Sea where applicable
- One anchor
- One sea anchor (drogue) when necessary to assist in manoeuvring

Some small, light-weight anchors such as these by the manufacturer Plastimo are available:

Photo: Grapnel Anchor   Photo: Hook Anchor

A sea-anchor is a small parachute-type safety device, which can be used in conditions of strong wind and high waves, which would force the boat/seaplane to lie parallel to the waves making it very unstable laterally (inducing lateral rolling into the troughs of the waves and bringing a high risk of submersion). The parachute drogue attaches to the stern of the boat and functions by forcing the bow of a boat/seaplane back into wind, thus providing much more stability in very dangerous conditions.

Photo: Para-tech sea drogue attached to a small boat in rough weather

In addition to the mandatory equipment, the following practical additions/ amendments are suggested:

- Life jacket: this must be the manually inflatable type, since automatically inflated types can pose a real hazard when trying to exit the aircraft from an enclosed cockpit. (Flexwings and other open-canopy aircraft have the advantage here). Although the requirement is that this should be 'readily accessible', ideally it should be donned prior to flight.
- If the life jacket is equipped with a whistle, this will also meet the requirement to have a 'sound signal' device on board.
- Anchor/sea anchor - see examples above, but remember to keep within the restrictions of MTOW (always an issue for microlights).
- Paddle(s) - safely stowed in the paddle bracket or in the cockpit area - these can assist enormously when manoeuvring at a dock.
- Hand-held, all-round light - assuming the aircraft is not fitted with lights - for taxying before/after sunset or in poor visibility.
- Emergency repair kit (for the appropriate float/hull composition).
- Mooring lines - neatly coiled
- Signalling flags/flares.
- Water proof communications - radio or mobile phone.

Photo: passenger with lifejacket awaiting flight. Life-jackets by law must be 'readily accessible' at all times, but in practice it is safer to ensure that every person on board dons a life jacket prior to boarding, since an emergency on the water or capsize is unlikely to offer much spare time for retrieving/donning the life jacket before actually entering the water.

Finally, thought should be given to ballast required. A floatplane usually has a CG slightly forward of centre, making it nose heavy, whilst a flying boat usually has a CG slightly aft of centre, making it tail heavy. The idea is to position ballast in a suitable place for the type. In a flying boat this would be at the most forward part of the cockpit. The requirement for ballast may vary depending on loading (passenger and fuel) so always consult the POH. Again, be aware of weight limits and staying within the MTOW.

Flexwing Considerations

Flexwing seaplanes, just like their 3-axis counterparts, are also available as floatplanes or flying boats. In the case of floatplanes, the type of float attached is usually a lighter-weight variation of the type described above. One important difference is the use of dual-stepped floats. These are not universally used, but are recommended for flexwing aircraft. The reason is that whilst with a fixed wing you can control the position of the floats in the water (once moving fast enough) by balancing with the elevator on the step, on a flexwing the wing can move independently from the floats and you cannot control the position of the floats in the water in the same way as with a fixed wing.

Photo: Mainair Alpha fitted with dual-step Russian floats.
Note also the large spray guard mounted between the floats to protect the propeller from spray damage.

That is not to say that some flexwing seaplanes operate with a single step (e.g. Antares). However, after applying full power the float will initially plough through the water with the stern very low, only pulling itself out of the water as one accelerates. The float then comes out of the water on the single step AND the aft portion of the float (as it cannot be balanced only on the single step).

With a dual-step float system the float will come out of the water more level and balanced on the front and rear steps simultaneously. This is considered to be more stable and allows slower take off speeds.

Flexwing flying boats, which are the most common flexwing seaplane in current production, use either an 'inflatable' rib-style boat, such as Lomac, or a fibreglass boat which tends to be wider and hence a little more stable. Both of these types are available as amphibians. There are several types of floats available for flexwings, including Krucker aluminium floats, Russian rubber floats (which are huge and like a pair of rocket-shaped pontoons - see photo above) and Cosmos composite floats.

Due to the fact that flexwings usually have rear-mounted engines, spray can be a major problem regarding its effect on the propeller. This is exacerbated by any manoeuvre that causes the stern of the aircraft to dig into the water, including plough taxying, as a result of which this manoeuvre is not recommended on flexwing seaplanes. Most types are fitted with spray rails of one kind or another; for example, see the photo above with spray cover fitted between the Russian floats.

Finally, note the requirements for safety equipment on board and bear in mind not only the MTOW allowed, but also the necessity to safely stow such equipment, within the limitations that an open cockpit aircraft offers.

Chapter 2

Taxying and Manoeuvring on the Water

Photo: Amphibious Storch, Lake Orsa, Sweden

Introduction

Most people might imagine that the biggest difference between a seaplane and a landplane is the ability to take off and land on water. This of course is true, but it is whilst manoeuvring on the water itself that the real handling differences between the two become apparent. Water is a fluid, which acts in a similar way to the air, so most of what you have learned about the movement of air will be applicable to the water also. However, that means that your taxying environment now resembles the air you fly in, with all its vagaries!

The water environment is infinitely changeable and challenging. This is because:

- Each wave is different.
- The wind is constantly changing subtly in direction and strength.
- The seaplane is affected by water depth, currents, surface waves, swells and fetch.
- Obstacles and objects may not always be immediately visible.

The first thing you will become aware of is the fact that on the water you have no brakes. That's right … the moment you fire up the engine you will be moving. Therefore it is more important than ever to keep mentally 'ahead' of the aircraft. You simply cannot afford not to think through what will happen as soon as you start the engine and immediately afterwards. Precisely how much and in what direction the aircraft will start to move will depend on a number of factors which will be different every time you set off.

Imagine the runway at your regular airfield; grass probably, or maybe you are spoiled and have tarmac. It will be laid out in pretty much a straight line and marked with clear white lines or regularly spaced cones. There may be a few small irregularities: a little upslope at one end and maybe a small furrow in the middle. The area where the numbers are painted is a little rough too and so you tend to line up to the right or to the left of the numbers to avoid the bumps. But these little imperfections are well known to you and remain constant. The slight upslope on RW06 is not going to change without notice to a slight down-slope. The numbers will not move to the right or to the left just as you are about to take off. And no-one is going to drive a speedboat across your path just before you rotate.

Now imagine your runway has turned to water - not just the runway itself but the whole airfield. You have a bigger manoeuvring area and you will be able to take off directly into the wind. So far, so good. But now you have to share the enlarged runway with other sea-going bodies: boats, swimmers, birds, floating debris and half-submerged planks of wood. Who has right of way? And what about that motorboat that was well behind you when you did your checks, but now has crept up fast on your starboard side to take a closer look at you?

Photos: harbours quiet and busy. Watch out for traffic movements even at quiet harbours like this one (on the left) in Sweden. At busy Poole harbour in Dorset (right photo), a summer afternoon can have boat movements thick on the water.

Suffice to say, the number of variables increases dramatically as soon as you fly from water. This should not put anyone off: it is a large part of what makes water flying so challenging and rewarding. It is a matter of being aware of all the possible factors to affect the seaplane, being prepared and taking prompt action to deal with any situation that arises.

Above all: the key thing is to respect the water environment as much as you respect the air above it.

Factors which affect the Seaplane on the Water
Water Drag

When an aircraft operates on land its wheels come into contact with the ground and through the friction thus created there is a certain degree of drag. However the ground is only in contact with 3 small 'patches' of the aircraft - the three wheels. When an aircraft operates on water, more or less the whole of the hull (in the case of a flying boat) or the two floats - in either case a considerable surface area - are in contact with the water. There is therefore far more drag to overcome.

To assist in overcoming the drag, the bottom of a seaplane hull or float is specially designed with a break point at around the point of the CG - called The Step. The step allows the seaplane to plane at high speed on the water and then to 'unstick' from the water by allowing air to enter underneath the hull(s). Without this the seaplane would never break free from the water surface. When you first apply full power to commence the take off run the stern of the hull or floats will initially dig into the water and the nose will rise. Continuing with full power and having the correct stick or control bar position (more on this later) will allow the seaplane to 'rise onto the step'. Having achieved this step attitude - which is fairly flat on the water - the aircraft can then accelerate to flying speed.

Photo: The Step section on this Storch float can clearly be seen just beneath the rear strut.

Wind

Wind needs to be considered in terms of its direction, strength and effect on the water. When operating on a large body of water it is always desirable to take off and land as closely into the wind as possible. Taking off crosswind carries more dangers than is experienced on a landplane. Why this is and techniques for dealing with a crosswind will be discussed later.

The wind direction can be determined by a number of factors. Firstly, waves themselves tend to form perpendicular to the wind. Additionally, where the wind blows from land towards the water there is nearly always a 'lee patch', which will become apparent on one part of the shoreline, indicating that the wind is coming from this direction.

Photo: In this picture, lee areas can be seen on the right-hand side of the islands and along the left-hand shoreline, indicating a wind coming from the left of the picture.

Other good indicators are flags (particularly near a boat harbour or marina) and moored boats, which will weathervane into the wind providing the wind is light. In a strong wind with large waves they will tend to align parallel with the swells. Also, if there is a current, boats tend to point into the current (unless the wind is much stronger than the current). Seabirds also tend to alight into wind and remain oriented that way on the water. Soaring birds, with wings outstretched, will ride on air currents facing the wind direction.

The strength of the wind (and any gusts) will affect our decision whether to fly or not, as ever in aviation. The effect of wind on the water is what gives us the indicators we need to make this judgement. (Since we can take off into wind, it is not necessarily the strength of the wind itself that would be the problem). Gusts will show up as dark patches on the water, often fanning outwards downwind of the gust. These are known as 'cats' paws' because they resemble the outstretched claws of a cat. Just like the claws of a cat they are best avoided! They can indicate very turbulent and unpredictable conditions and should be avoided for take off and landing. Sometimes long, straight, dark-coloured or foam-topped streaks can be seen which run parallel to the wind. These indicate a strong but more laminar wind which can be good for taking off and landing because they indicate strong but stable wind conditions.

Photo: on approach to this small lake, the 'cat's paws' showing up as dark, claw-like streaks on the water indicate strong gusts. Extreme caution required on landing.

Waves, Fetch and Swell

Waves are a product of wind acting on the water. On a windless day on a lake you will see what is known as 'glassy water' conditions. If the day is perfectly calm you will see a mirror-image of the sky and surrounding shoreline in the water. (This is rarely encountered on the sea, since the sea is such a huge body of water that it is affected by wind and weather occurring very long distances away, and also by the effect of tides).

Photo: truly glassy conditions, Lake Orsa, Sweden.

A light wind will produce small ripples; the stronger the wind the bigger will be the waves. The Beaufort Scale (Appendix A) gives a good indication of the type of wave to be expected with different wind strengths.

Larger waves (those produced by a wind of 8 knots or more) will have their crests blown off them forming foam or 'white caps/white horses' as they are variously known. The bigger the waves, the more likely we will have problems in a seaplane. Large or even medium-sized waves can submerge a float or sponson and cause capsize if we are not quick to correct the situation. The correct action to take in this case would be to turn the aircraft towards the submerged float (probably counter-intuitive to most of us) in order to generate more lift on the float that is still flying. If we tried to do the opposite, i.e. to lift the submerged float by turning the other way, we would simply make the situation worse by slowing down the still-flying float and speeding up the submerged float which would then submerge faster.

Wave patterns are set up by the wind and can continue for some time after the wind changes, especially if the wind has been quite strong and produced large waves. Waves that persist in this manner are known as swells and they may be some distance from their actual source. If the wind changes direction, a new wave pattern will be set up, superimposed on the existing wave pattern. Wave patterns are generally easy to see from above but may be difficult to ascertain from the ground or shore line.

Photo: two different wave patterns superimposed on top of each other,
causing a criss-cross pattern to emerge.

The size that waves become depends on the wind strength, already mentioned, and also the size of the body of water, i.e. the area on which the wind can act. For example a large lake may develop high waves downwind close to the far shore. A smaller lake with the same wind will develop smaller waves. The distance covered by the wind on the water is known as the Fetch.

Photo: waves perpendicular to the beach show that the wind is flowing along the shoreline.
Two boats at anchor pointing into the wind give the wind direction. (A third boat is beached).

Current - Rivers and Outlets

On a river or around the mouth of an estuary the seaplane is subject to currents. Dealing with currents is an advanced topic and something the beginner pilot should avoid in practice until very experienced with the fundamentals of seaplane flying. However, learning to deal with currents is an important part of sea flying and gaining experience in this area at the appropriate point gives an invaluable added dimension.

In brief, operating on a current means that the body of water is itself moving, not just the waves on the surface. Current affects the seaplane in a similar way to the wind. For example, taxying with the current (i.e. downstream) you will have a fast ground speed, similar to flying downwind. Taxying up current is similar to flying upwind (i.e. slower), so it is desirable to taxy up current when coming into dock and when making tight manoeuvres. Turning from up current to down current means you will have to watch your down current drift, a situation which has parallels with turning from upwind to downwind.

The above situations, without any wind, are very straightforward. However if you also have to contend with the wind itself, which may be blowing in the same direction as the current, or in opposition to it, or at any angle across it, the situation can become very complex. If you consider the current as a 'secondary wind' - on the water surface itself - you will have some idea of the complications. For example, landing with the current (downstream) gives the slowest possible touch down speed. However, if the wind is in the same direction as the current, should one continue to land downstream or upstream, into the wind? Since the current is what affects you the most after landing, a general rule of thumb is to give priority to the current unless the wind is significantly stronger than the current, in which case give priority to the wind.

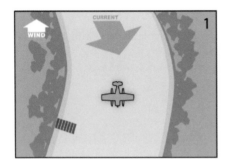 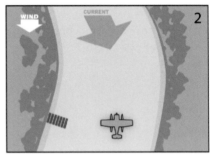

In diagram 1 above, the current is flowing down the river towards the sea but the wind is blowing in the opposite direction. This is an advantageous situation as you can land slowly with the current and into the wind. In diagram 2, the wind and current are from the same direction. Which way to land will mainly depend on the relative strengths of the current and the wind. With a light current and strong wind, landing into wind would be preferable.

Further thought must be given to the matter of docking after landing. Again the matter of wind versus current are pertinent: you should always avoid a situation whereby the wind or current can blow or push you hard into a dock risking damage to the seaplane. In diagram 2 you are at risk both from the wind and the current, so aim to land well south of the dock and taxy to the downwind side of the dock for mooring. In diagram 1 you will have to assess which of the wind or current is most likely to affect you in the vicinity of the dock. The current may be lighter at the side of the shore than in the middle of the river. The wind is likely to be the same strength, although there may be a sheltered area by the shore.

As you can see, there are an infinite number of variables to these scenarios, depending on the wind and current direction and strength. Now try to imagine some of these scenarios in a tight manoeuvring area with obstacles in the water and you start to see the sort of problems that may be experienced after landing. As already mentioned, this is an advanced topic! See more on docking in Chapter 5.

Tides

A tide is nothing more than a current due to the inflow of water into a bay or channel. This can be at sea or on a large inland waterway. A tide will rise and fall at given times twice during the day. The timing of this will vary with location and these 'tide times' are predictable enough to be documented and made available in tide tables or nautical almanacs for planning purposes. You can also find tide predictions on marine websites, searchable by port and date.

Each day the tide will be approximately 50 minutes later than the previous day. The astronomical reasons for this are very interesting, but they are too big a subject for this book. The greatest current will be at mid-tide, and the least at low and high tide. Tidal currents can be very strong, depending on their location and situation, so it is important to acquire local knowledge to take them into account and plan accordingly.

The following is an excerpt of tidal predictions from the UK Hydrographic Office website (www.ukho.gov.uk) for the port of Southampton for 2 days:

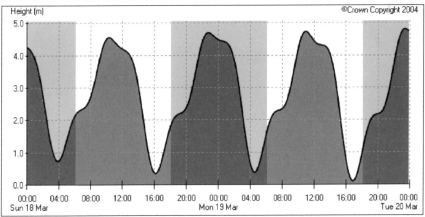

Sun 18 Mar				Mon 19 Mar			
LW	HW	LW	HW	LW	HW	LW	HW
03:47	10:04	16:09	22:29	04:30	10:45	16:52	23:09
0.7 m	4.5 m	0.3 m	4.7 m	0.4 m	4.7 m	0.1 m	4.8 m

Predicted heights are in metres above Chart Datum

The data shows the dates for the prediction, tide height at 4 hourly intervals in graphical form and high and low water tide times and corresponding heights.

Taxying a Seaplane
General

With all seaplanes it is desirable to take off and land as much into wind as possible. This is so that the relevant airflow is coming from the front, which reduces take off time and landing roll. It also creates a more stable condition for the seaplane on the water.

Even when merely taxying - with no intention of taking off - it is vital to be aware of where the wind is coming from. This is to avoid getting into a situation where the wind and conditions could conspire to act on our aircraft in such a way that could lead to a possible capsize. This is especially important for flexwing types, where the big wing area is like a huge umbrella. Therefore the considerations regarding 'relevant airflow' are discussed more fully in the section 'Flexwing Considerations'.

Taxying Techniques

Photos of Polaris FIB in 3 different taxy modes:

There are 3 types of taxy technique, as illustrated above:

1. **Idle taxy (boat flat on the water, no spray)**
2. **Plough taxy (stern deep in water, considerable spray)**
3. **Step taxy (boat flat on water, little spray)**

1. Idle or displacement taxy: power setting is idle or low, giving just a few knots over the water. The boat is flat on the water. The water rudder is down and manoeuvrability (providing the winds are fairly light) should be good. Forward visibility is also good and spray is minimal. Noise is low - which could be a factor in sensitive areas. This form of taxying is used whenever possible, but especially when close to objects and the shoreline, in areas of restricted movement, when you wish to keep the noise down or when there is not far to taxy.

2. Plough taxy: the power setting is quite high, pushing the bow upwards and the stern deeper into the water. With the nose of the aircraft thus raised, the centre of buoyancy (COB) of the aircraft - which is the average point of support - moves aft and a considerable proportion of the aircraft fuselage (3-axis types) is exposed to the wind, which can assist in turning the aircraft downwind within a small turning radius. This, in fact, is the main use for this technique: turning from upwind to downwind when the wind would be strong enough to prevent it without the application of additional power, as a consequence of the natural weather-cocking tendency of the seaplane. However, the disadvantages are that spray can be considerable, possibly causing damage to the propeller if the propeller is rear-mounted (*see* **Flexwing Considerations**) and forward visibility in 3-axis aircraft is poor due to the high nose attitude.

3. Fast or step taxy: fast taxying is initiated by applying full power with the stick held fully back (in 3-axis aircraft). In the light aircraft world, it is always considered necessary to retract the water rudders to prevent unwanted drag and damage. Drag is less of an issue than stability with very small seaplanes (though damage is still a risk), so in certain types only the water rudder should be left down. With full power applied, the aircraft nose will rise in either one or two stages, depending on type: this is called the 'hump' phase. When this stage is reached the stick pressure is released to the degree that the weight of the aircraft is transferred forwards, and the boat is then planing flat on the water. To avoid taking off (assuming that is not the aim) the rpm is reduced to about three-quarters power. Use fast taxying when you have large amounts of water to cover and when noise and close objects in the water are not an issue. However, note that fast taxying downwind in strong and gusty conditions is not normally recommended.

Turns while Taxying

We have talked about taxying in a general sense but when it comes to positioning for take off it is necessary to manoeuvre the aircraft carefully with due attention to the wind. Ideally you will already have assessed the wind conditions and any restrictions on the water in relation to the wind direction. In normal circumstances it is advisable to take off as much into the wind as possible. With experience and ideally after practice with a qualified instructor, you can learn to take off in a curving pattern or with a 'dog-leg', which is a useful skill for taking off in a restricted area or with a crosswind.

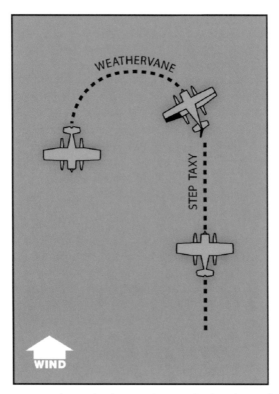

Diagram: step taxy downwind to the required position, then bring the aircraft to idle and allow the seaplane to weathervane into wind for the take off roll.

Let us for now deal with the 'normal' scenario. If you have to turn from downwind to an upwind position in order to start your take-off run your best course of action is to complete your downwind taxi run and, assuming this was a step taxi, reduce the power to idle, lower the water rudder and allow the aircraft to weathercock into the wind. See the diagram above. Correct positioning of the controls during this turn is important. In a 3-axis aircraft, having reduced power to idle, the elevator is kept fully back whilst the into-wind aileron should be held up as the aircraft obligingly weathervanes. Use whatever rudder position is necessary to control the turn. Same-side rudder may initially be required, followed by neutralised rudder and even opposite rudder if the wind is very strong, in order to avoid the aircraft swinging around too fast. As the nose comes round into the wind the stick is maintained fully back while the ailerons are centralised.

It is important to note that you should never make a fast (step) turn from downwind to upwind in a floatplane (in some flying boats it is permissible). Why is this? The diagram below illustrates the problem. Basically there are two forces which we need to consider when making a turn. The first force is centrifugal force, which, when we turn, tries to oppose the direction of the turn by making the seaplane continue its original path. Secondly there is the force of the wind, which as we turn from downwind to the upwind position will be acting on the fuselage broadside on to the wind. This force combined with the centrifugal force can easily be enough to turn us over. Even if we use into-wind aileron it is simply not enough to counteract these forces. Obviously the stronger the wind, the tighter we turn and the faster we taxy, the greater will be the forces acting on us in the turn. However, even in a light wind we should avoid turning from down to upwind, in order to instil the correct habit. So remember the rule: from downwind to upwind allow the natural tendency of the seaplane to weathercock itself into the wind, avoiding one of the most likely capsize situations.

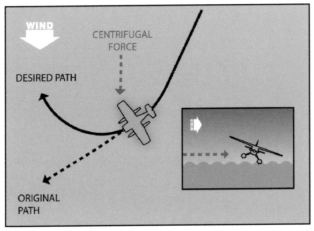

Diagram: centrifugal force and wind force acting on seaplane in a turn to upwind

Note that the same problem may not arise in a small flying boat, however it is important to check for each type. This is because a flying boat hull is more laterally stable on the water, with a lower CG, and therefore is not likely to be tipped over by the forces mentioned above. In a 3-axis flying boat, the turn should be made using into-wind rudder and some opposite aileron as necessary to keep the wing-tip float from getting too low on the into-wind side and possibly getting buried in the water. See also **Flexwing Considerations** for more on this subject.

When turning from upwind to downwind in a moderate wind there is no problem. The 2 forces mentioned above will cancel each other out and the turn can be made safely, using the correct into-wind aileron technique. When making this turn in strong wind conditions be careful not to turn past your intended point, since the aircraft will try to weathercock back into the wind behind and you might not be able to stay on a downwind heading. Anticipate this by aiming to turn slightly short of 180 degrees and resuming downwind with a slight increase in power.

Turn Radius

If we use a high speed step-taxy turn (from upwind to downwind) we will cover considerable ground - or rather water - before completing the turn. This is different from what we would expect when making a turn in the air. In the latter case, increased power would reduce our turn radius but in a seaplane we are 'attached' to the water surface and so our turn radius increases with power. One consequence is that we need to consider the available area and whether we have sufficient space. If we need to make a small radius turn in these circumstances (to avoid shoreline or obstacles) we should choose either an idle taxy turn, or alternatively a plough turn if the wind is too strong to turn in the idle taxy mode.

Torque Effect

A further consideration is engine torque. If there is considerable torque-effect on a particular aircraft type this will assist in turning the aircraft in a particular direction. The turn radius will consequently be smaller. If the aircraft is a mono-hull the torque effect may be accompanied by a certain amount of tilting (like a boat) which will further accelerate the turn. Note that when the intention is to taxi in straight line, torque effect must be counteracted by correct use of rudder.

Rudder Efficiency

This is affected by speed through the water. Generally speaking, the faster a seaplane is taxying, the more effective the rudder will be. At very low speeds, on some types, the water rudder can be very ineffective. It is important to check for rudder efficiency before attempting to manoeuvre in a tight area.

Porpoising

This can occur when the seaplane is not maintained in the correct trim position during a step taxy. The ensuing condition, where the aircraft pitches and heaves, is known as porpoising. This situation can become very dangerous if not corrected within one or two oscillations. (A bit like allowing an aircraft to bounce after landing ... the third bounce will probably be a crash).

Porpoising can occur when the nose is allowed to rise too high or drop too low. To correct it, either apply back pressure when the bows are rising, or forward pressure when they are dropping. The correction must be made immediately and at the right moment, i.e. in phase with the oscillations, otherwise it could exacerbate the situation instead of improving it. Alternatively, a small increase in power may be all that is required, since inadvertently reducing power may have caused the seaplane to come off the step and to commence porpoising.

Unless you are confident of the correct action (which comes with experience) then the best move is to come off the throttle and pull the stick fully back. This stops the step taxying and the porpoising. With everything under control again, simply re-start the taxying procedure paying closer attention to the stick position.

Bouncing

Photo: high waves like this could cause bouncing. Keep to a low power setting until in calmer water.

Bouncing may occur as a result of severe porpoising (see above) or simply through taxying on high waves, which bounce the aircraft into the air, from crest to crest. It is an uncomfortable experience and one which may make you think twice about setting off in rough water conditions again! Of vital importance is maintaining control of the aircraft attitude, with a slight lowering of the nose when the aircraft is bounced into the air, and a slight raising of the nose before the aircraft hits the next wave. Strong winds and gusts accompanying high waves are likely to make pitch control even more difficult. Consider carefully before venturing out in these conditions.

Flexwing Considerations
Taxying

Taxying a flexwing aircraft has to be done with even more care than a 3-axis aircraft for it is possible for the wind to get underneath the wing and this, combined with a (possibly) higher CG and the tilting effects of waves can combine to tip the aircraft over. The wing in this case acts like a big umbrella and we all know what can happen to umbrellas in a gale.

Diagram: effect of strong wind getting underneath FIB wing. In diagram 1, the flying boat wing is level with the water. In diagram 2, the wind has picked up and is blowing strongly from the side. The pilot tilts the wing to stop the wind getting underneath. In diagram 3, the pilot has inadvertently allowed the wind to get underneath the wing and lift it. Diagram 4 shows the possible result: the wind pushes against the large under-surface area of the wing and pushes it over.

Let us go back to basics for a moment in order to consider relevant airflow. Think what happens when you are sitting in a moving car and you put a hand out of the window. You will feel the air hitting your hand from the front. Does that mean that you are driving into the wind? Of course not. The wind could be blowing from any direction. It could even be a calm day with no wind but you will still feel the airflow from the front. The point is that the car (and therefore your hand) is moving faster than the air around it, causing you to feel the airflow coming towards you.

If you are on the water in no wind and you start to taxy forwards you will immediately create a relevant airflow from the front. It is important to realize that to have a forward relative speed you must be taxying fast enough to overcome any wind from the side or rear; it is not enough to count on airspeed (or groundspeed in this case) alone. If the wind is quite strong from behind you may have to taxi quite a way to pick up enough speed to get a forward relative wind.

If the wind is from behind, keep the bar slightly forwards whilst taxying to prevent the wind getting underneath the trailing edge. It is best to taxy fast in this scenario to keep the aircraft as stable as possible. With the wing almost at flying speed (even whilst still on the water) stability is greatly increased.

Note that in a flexwing flying boat, the rudder is kept down at all times when on the water as a further aid to stability. The practice of raising the rudder for a high speed taxy is not recommended, since the advantage of stability outweighs the disadvantage of additional drag.

Photo: note the rudder in the down position on both of these Polaris FIBs.
Notice also the 'cage' around the propeller …. to provide some protection for unwary on-lookers.

In the case of a crosswind, keep the windward wing tipped down a little to avoid the wind getting underneath. Get up to speed quickly and be aware of the wing (bar) position at all times - it is the most important aspect by far of taxying on the water. If you are making a turn you will need to adjust the bar position promptly as you turn into or away from the wind.

Remember you may be taxying at low speeds when manoeuvring to a dock for example, or if there are boats and swimmers in the vicinity. In this situation you will not be able to taxy fast to achieve stability and you may not at all times be heading into the wind. If the wind itself is moderate or strong and coming from the side or rear then the problems will be compounded.

Unlike in a 3-axis machine where the wing is fixed to the fuselage, a trike wing moves independently from the aircraft. In some senses this is an advantage: we can move the wing against the wind to a greater degree than we could position the ailerons in the same way on a fixed-wing machine. We would run out of aileron authority on a 3-axis aircraft well before we utilise the whole range of movement on a flexwing. With a flexwing aircraft we can move the windward wing considerably into the wind, adjusting it according to the strength of the wind and the degree of off-wind component. However, it requires good piloting skills to use this range of movement effectively and to be constantly reacting to the changing position of the aircraft on the water.

One of the problems, particularly for new pilots, is that from our early childhood we learn to think that whatever is underneath our feet - whether we are standing or sitting - is parallel to the horizon. In other words, if we are sitting in a boat then the bottom of the boat is parallel to the horizon. This is particularly relevant in a flying boat, where the hull of the boat is quite v-shaped, allowing it to roll with the waves and turns. This makes it very sea-worthy in that it will automatically compensate for the sea-state and can therefore withstand bigger waves and rougher seas than would swamp and risk capsize in a twin-floated aircraft. But unless we compensate for this rolling by tipping the wing to remain parallel to the horizon - or even a little down into the wind - we run the risk of being tipped over by the wind getting underneath. This can happen from the side (underneath the wing tips) or the rear (under the trailing edge) though it is most likely caused by a side wind.

So the most important thing in taxying a flexwing is always to be aware of the wind direction, particularly when turning and co-ordinate our handling of the bar accordingly. If you are unsure, keep checking for wind indicators on the shoreline and glance frequently at the wing-tips to check the wing is level. A ribbon or 'tell tale' fixed in strategic position on the front strut will also help to indicate where the relative wind is coming from at any given time.

Photo: ribbon attached to the front flying wire of a Polaris FIB indicates the relative wind
(in this picture, the wind is almost calm)

Turns while Taxying
Torque

In the previous section we mentioned the effects of torque while turning. In a flying boat torque and boat tilt will act together in one direction (normally to the left) producing a small-radius turn. This is not a problem in a 3-axis aircraft, but in a flexwing flying boat don't forget you will need to move the wing considerably to keep it level with the horizon. If you turn in the opposite direction to the torque effect, the torque and tilt will cancel each other out and you will have to move the wing less. Although the turn radius will be greater the turn will feel more comfortable, especially in strong wind conditions.

Strong Winds

Another option when needing to manoeuvre with a strong wind (for example after landing) is to reduce the power to idle and allow the wind to push you to the shore. This avoids having to make a turn in difficult conditions and controlling the wing while doing so. If you have the means to tie the wings down on each side take advantage of this and if necessary use a paddle to maintain directional control.

Plough Turns

Most flexwing seaplanes have rear-mounted engines which means that the propeller is close to the water and vulnerable to spray damage. Some floatplane flexwing aircraft have spray guards attached between the two floats to minimise the spray damage. Where these are not fitted, or in the case of a flexwing flying boat, a turn using the plough taxy method would push the stern deep into the water and maximise the possibility of water-spray damage. For this reason, the plough taxy technique is not recommended for this seaplane type.

Downwind to Upwind

Whilst this must not be attempted in a 3-axis floatplane, it can be done in a flexwing seaplane, since the wing can be manoeuvred downwards during the turn, preventing the wind pushing the aircraft over. This is best done at high speed (step taxying) so that the aircraft is at its most stable on the water. However, it should not be attempted if gusty wind conditions or high waves exist, due to the difficulty in maintaining control of the wing sufficiently in such conditions.

Chapter 3

Taking Off

Photos: Polaris FIB and Thruster aircraft just after taking off.

In the previous chapter we discussed manoeuvring on the water and the importance of developing a feel for water conditions. The take off area must be carefully surveyed before lining up so that a safe path for the take off roll can be secured. Even when taking off from a home base or known body of water, heavy rain, tides or debris from surrounding shorelines may have deposited objects which could cause a problem for a seaplane whose speed is increasing during the take off roll. Additionally, it is good practice to do an Engine Failure After Take Off (EFATO) briefing prior to take off, once the take off area has been established. This prepares the pilot for an engine failure just after take off and in the climb at low altitude.

Having established the area is clear, the type of take off will be determined by the sea and wind conditions and the size/shape of the body of water. We will deal with the following different scenarios:

1. **Normal Water**
2. **Glassy Water**
3. **Rough Water**
4. **Cross Wind**
5. **Restricted/Confined Areas**

Normal Water

Photo: Airborne Streak fitted with Antares floats on 'normal water'.
Waves are distinct but small without any white caps.

Water is classed as 'normal' when it has small and fairly uniform ripples, normally force 2-3 on the Beaufort Scale. At the upper end of this range a few white caps may become visible, but these should be few and far between. The aircraft is manoeuvred into wind (remembering the dangers of taxying from downwind to upwind) and final checks are quickly made. A frequently used check list mnemonic from the light aircraft world is FCARS:

- Flap Set
- Carb. Heat Cold
- Area Clear
- Rudder Up
- Stick Back

This can be modified to CARS, FARS or ARS depending on what features are available on the particular seaplane. In an aircraft equipped with flaps, the first stage of flap is normal, but always refer to the POH. Flying boats with flaps, being lower in the water than floatplanes, may have the flaps fully retracted until on the step to avoid spray damage whilst getting onto the step. Then select stage 1 flap whilst step-taxying.

Holding the stick fully back whilst smoothly applying full power, the aircraft nose will rise - steeply in some cases - so that the stern is deep in the water. It is important to keep the stick fully back and the aircraft balanced using aileron and rudder. With forward vision temporarily impeded by the high attitude, use peripheral vision to keep the aircraft straight on the water. Depending on seaplane type, this attitude can cause a large amount of spray to be created, however the nose-high attitude is mercifully short since the seaplane will quickly reach its highest point (known as 'the hump') after 1 or 2 stages of nose-rise, at which time the stick can be relaxed to a more or less neutral position and the bow settles to a flat, planing position on the water known as being 'on the step'. It is important now to keep the aircraft straight using rudder as required. To assist this, use a feature ahead - possibly on a distant shore - as a reference.

Some seaplanes will require a slight decrease in back pressure on the stick to achieve the step position whilst others arrive there more or less by themselves. Once this step position (also known as the 'sweet spot') is reached, it is now very important to keep the aircraft in the same attitude until flying speed is achieved and the aircraft lifts off.

Photos: Thruster getting up on the step (photo 1) and fully on the step (photo 2).
Note considerable spray created when the nose is high in photo 1 and much less spray
(and hence less drag) coming from further aft when the aircraft is properly on the step.

The correct planing position is where there is least resistance or drag on the aircraft hull or floats. This takes a while to get used to and must be practised to get it right every time. If the stick is too far forwards and the nose is low there will be more resistance from the water on the floats/hull and there is a likelihood that speed will diminish. This will make it harder to achieve take off speed and may lead to porpoising.

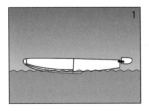 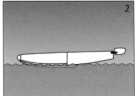 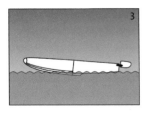

It is important to maintain the correct attitude while step-taxying. Diagrams: 1. float on water in correct step attitude; 2. nose too low; 3. nose too high.

On the other hand, if the stick is too far back and the nose too high, the tail of the floats or hull will be dragging in the water, again causing increased resistance. This can often happen where a pilot tries to haul the aircraft out of the water too early. However this will simply increase resistance further and exacerbate the problem. The corrective action would be to allow the nose to lower slightly so that the 'sweet spot' is resumed and flying speed can be achieved.

Once safely clear of the water hold the correct attitude to achieve climb speed with the nose slightly lowered as normal in low-inertia aircraft. Then when out of ground-effect adjust the attitude to the correct climb attitude and climb to the height required. Retract the flaps if used. In the case of an amphibian flying from land, without the intention to land on water during the flight, raise the undercarriage once a safe height is achieved (and appropriate landing options are available). Amphibians are often fitted with strategically placed mirrors to enable a visual check of the landing gear.

Glassy Water

Photo: a beautiful scene but the mirror-like conditions pose a problem for judging the landing.

The characteristics of glassy water were discussed in the previous chapter. To recap, these are conditions where the water is a complete or partial mirror, or where the ripples are fairly indistinct with a surface appearance that is more 'wobbly' than rippled. Glassy water can be difficult to take off from, because the flat water adheres to the under surface of the hull or floats to the extent that the aircraft cannot easily break away from the surface. The water is literally sucking the boat to its surface.

This means that the take off run will be longer, so it is important to assess the amount of water required to achieve take off. An area that is adequate in normal water conditions may prove too short when glassy conditions prevail.

However, there are one or two techniques to assist with glassy water takeoffs. In the case of an aircraft with floats, after coming onto the step a float may be lifted out of the water, by the appropriate use of aileron e.g. moving the stick to the left causes an increase in lift on the right wing which makes the right float lift; right rudder is then applied carefully to keep the seaplane tracking straight. Depending on which float is lifted in this way, torque effect may assist (in which case more directional control with rudder to counteract the turning tendency will be required).

Having one float out of the water reduces the water suction by half and so the aircraft will take off more readily. Once out of the water, ailerons and rudder are then adjusted to straighten the aircraft and the take off climb proceeds as normal.

This technique cannot be used with a flying boat hull, though in some types it is possible to 'rock' the aircraft longitudinally, to create a gap of air underneath the hull and help break the suction. This will depend very much on type and advice should be taken from a suitably experienced instructor.

Another technique, which may be applied by both floatplanes and flying boats, is to taxy downwind criss-crossing the intended take off path, in order to create some wake on the water. Line up into wind and take off across the wake thus created to allow air underneath the hull/float surface.

After take off the aircraft should be flown as normal, without lowering the nose after lift-off since without the normal textural references of the surface it is possible to fly the aircraft inadvertently straight back into the water.

Rough Water

Rough water is normally classed as Beaufort Scale 4 or higher, often with white caps and/or streaks and 'cats paws' on the water surface. Take off may be shorter due to the strong winds, but the aircraft can be bounced on the crests of the waves, making for an uncomfortable ride and risking, among other things, stalling at a low height above the water, having a float submerged by a large wave and damaging the various float attachments and fittings.

When rough water conditions exist thought should be given to the wisdom of taking off at all. If the decision to go ahead has been taken, then consideration should be given to finding the best possible area of water in nearby surrounds. However, extensive taxying on rough water in order to find a better take off area is also to be avoided. In small, light seaplanes the risks of being submerged by waves, damage done to the floats or attachments, or being tipped over due to excessive rocking around on high waves is not to be underestimated. Not to mention that all this is very uncomfortable and any passenger is unlikely to be impressed!

Once facing into wind the take off should be similar to a soft field take off, in other words, aim to take off as early as possible with the lowest possible speed. The correct planing position, which will be achieved a little quicker than normal, will be at a slightly higher nose attitude than for normal water in order to prevent the front of the floats being submerged by a wave.

If the waves are sufficiently large the aircraft will bounce from wave crest to wave crest. Forward stick pressure should be applied to prevent the aircraft stalling after each bounce, and back pressure to avoid hitting the next wave nose-down, which could swamp the floats and lead to a capsize. Precise control of the aircraft attitude using the elevator is vital, so this is not a take off that should be undertaken lightly. After take off on the back of an upward wave movement, the nose should be lowered carefully to avoid a stall, but be careful not to lower the aircraft floats back into the high waves. The aircraft can be flown in ground effect at this lower than normal nose attitude to achieve a safe climbing airspeed and then climb away.

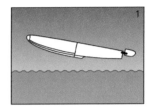 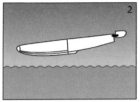 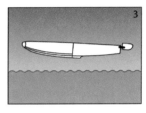

Diagram: float plane and the dangers of high waves on take off. Picture 1: with nose too high the aircraft can stall back onto the water; picture 2: with nose too low, the aircraft could hit the water nose down; picture 3: the aircraft could be bounced into the air and need precision control to land back in a safe attitude.

The technique for a flying boat hull is the same as the above, but the mono-hull is perhaps better suited to rough water, since it does not have individual floats which could be submerged. However, high waves can damage the sponsons and the battering and pounding from the rough water is still undesirable.

Cross Wind Takeoffs

Normally, one of the advantages of flying a seaplane is the ability to take off into the wind. Occasionally this is not possible, for example if operating in an area where the take off length required lies in a cross wind direction.

If the crosswind is light, a take off can be made using the normal technique for land planes with the aileron held down into wind as required and the rudder used to keep tracking straight. The take off roll will be longer compared to a take off into the wind. In a stronger crosswind, with increased into wind aileron applied, and for a longer period, there is the risk of submerging the downwind float as the aircraft gets onto the Step. Should there be any sense of this happening, the throttle must be cut (to reduce speed) and if necessary turn towards the submerging float. This slows the float down and therefore reduces the risk of it continuing to dive. If a float becomes 'buried' it is likely that the aircraft will roll and capsize, therefore prevention is paramount. If this is your only option for taking off, then aim to do it when wind conditions are more favourable. Remember that crosswind limitation for seaplanes is generally lower than for the equivalent landplane.

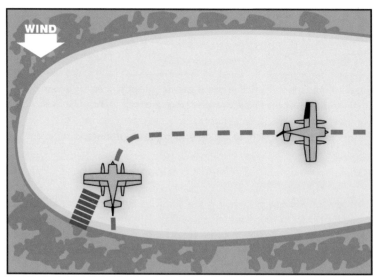

Diagram: take off path for a seaplane commencing into wind and turning crosswind.
Note the left aileron into the wind and right rudder to keep straight.

An alternative crosswind technique is to commence the take off roll into wind and then make a turn cross wind (assuming that this will provide the space required) whilst rolling the ailerons fully into the wind. After turning onto cross-wind get the aircraft onto the step whilst maintaining directional control by use of air rudder. The water rudders should be raised just before going onto the step. After takeoff, the aircraft should be turned into the wind (or partially so, allowing for any obstacles during climbout) to avoid the extra drag associated with a crabbed aircraft.

Restricted/Confined Areas

To avoid having to take off in too small an area, try not to land in such an area in the first place. Nevertheless, having found yourself in this situation plan to use all the available space on the water, rather like for a short field take off on land. Circular takeoffs are possible, but only with the right kind of seaplane - preferably a flying boat, which is far more laterally stable on the water than a floatplane. With this kind of seaplane a smaller turn radius is possible allowing for a longer straight take off path following a circular turn or even a take off during a shallow turn.

Remember however that a high speed turn directly from downwind to upwind could cause capsize should the wind and centrifugal force combine in sufficient strength, therefore this should be avoided, especially with a floatplane.

The problem with trying to take off from a confined area that has not been attempted before is that restrictive areas are not great places for experimentation. It takes considerable experience to know your aircraft sufficiently well, taking into account wind conditions, turbulence, density altitude, loading, shoreline obstacles and the aircraft performance, to be able to calculate if there is sufficient space for a safe take off and climb-out.

Once again, this is an advanced technique, one that is worth practising with an experienced seaplane instructor, preferably in a flying environment which, while indicative of the problems, still allows margin for error.

Photo: try not to land where you would not want to take off.

After Take-Off Procedures

Flying a seaplane is all about thinking ahead and being prepared. Consider the situation where you are taking off from a small lake and about to fly over land to your destination. You may trust the engine sufficiently to climb out and depart directly en route. But a safer option would be to remain close to the water until a safe height is reached, and then depart. What is a 'safe height'? That is a question that 'depends' for its answer on a number of factors: the aircraft type, the terrain below, the competence and currency of the pilot …. and so on.

One rule of thumb is, whatever your safety margin in a landplane, at least double it for a seaplane. For example, on climb out, a seaplane will experience more parasitic drag than an equivalent landplane due to the floats. This drag tends to reduce the airspeed and climb performance. The latter is important to be aware of, especially if flying in mountainous areas, since local conditions (turbulence, downdrafts) can cause problems for smaller seaplanes (as for any small aircraft), potentially without the power required to climb away.

Additionally, obstacles on the shore line (power cables, flag poles etc), distractions in unfamiliar terrain and an apparent increase in ground speed (e.g. as you turn from upwind to cross or down wind) can potentially cause the pilot to inadvertently raise the nose and reduce the airspeed to an unsafe level. If these circumstances combine when the aircraft has just left gliding distance of the water, you could find yourself in a very perilous situation.

Therefore plan your departure carefully before take off, ideally remaining close to the water until the height achieved is at least high enough to land back on the water effortlessly if necessary.

Don't leave the relative safety of the water area too quickly after take off. Instead gain height over the water.

Flexwing Considerations
General

In the flexwing seaplane the water rudder is normally left down for the take off roll in order to assist its stability in the water and retracted after take off to reduce drag whilst airborne.

A flexwing flying boat may have a strong tendency to turn either left or right due to torque effect when full power is applied in the take off roll. Initially the boat hull will tilt to one side and then commence a turn. It will be necessary to anticipate this and be ready to apply water rudder quickly to keep the boat in a straight line. Using a feature on the horizon will assist with this. Even more importantly, as the boat tilts the bar must be moved positively towards the tilted side in order to keep the wings level with the horizon. In other words, if the boat tilts left side down, move the bar further left to keep the bar level.

The bar may be held fully forwards (the equivalent of stick fully back on a 3-axis aircraft) or in a slightly more neutral position to aid stability (depending on type) until planing speed is reached, and moved to the right or left as appropriate to keep the wings level. Once on the step, the bar should be moved forwards to assist take off. After take off, the bar is returned to neutral and the wings are levelled, after which best rate of climb is established. The take off bar position may vary somewhat depending on type.

Photo: the boat is turning and tilting left and the pilot has moved
the bar to the left in order to keep the wings level.

Glassy Water

Depending on aircraft weight, loading and power plant, some types of flexwing seaplane can require 1km or more of 'runway' before the aircraft will take off in glassy conditions. Not only is this tedious and heavy on fuel, it can also be dangerous in the sense that it is impossible to adequately survey such a large area prior to commencing the take off roll. On the other hand, forward visibility is very good on this type of aircraft. A technique sometimes practised in such circumstances is for both the pilot and passenger to lean backwards as far as possible (whilst maintaining control of the bar and steering) to push the stern further into the water and the nose of the aircraft higher. This, combined with rocking the aircraft longitudinally by moving the bar quickly backwards and forwards, can shorten the take off run required by a considerable amount. You still have to maintain control of the aircraft however!

Rough Water

The relative lightness and vulnerability of a small flexwing aircraft should be enough to deter one from setting off in conditions that could easily capsize a bigger seaplane, without due skill and care being taken. Flexwing flying boats will be more capable of withstanding rough seas, since their hull is generally more robust and less easy to capsize than the equivalent floats. Nevertheless, it is necessary to control the aircraft wing with a high degree of skill, in possibly gusty conditions, whilst being bounced from wave to wave.

Photo: this flexwing flying boat could be vulnerable to large waves in a heavy swell.

Crosswind

The aircraft should be brought up to planing speed as fast as possible to ensure a positive forward airflow from the start and better rudder control. Ideally the aircraft should be manoeuvred so that the crosswind is from the opposite side to the turning tendency of the aircraft. The turning tendency will help to counteract some of the weather cocking tendency. The into-wind wing should be lowered slightly if the wind is moderate to strong, to prevent the wing being lifted. Aside from that, normal cross-wind considerations apply as on a landplane.

Chapter 4

The Approach and Landing

Photo: Skyranger just about to touch down

Selecting the Landing Area

To an even greater degree than landing on land, water landings must be carefully prepared for. No amount of preparation and checking is excessive when it comes to making the necessary overpasses to review the desired landing area when away from home base. Even at a familiar water base the conditions may have changed since taking off. In short, treat each seaplane landing like a precautionary landing and always, always be prepared to go around and land elsewhere.

Note that the low flying rule (Rule 5) does not apply to a seaplane inspecting a landing area, since that is considered a normal and prudent part of the landing process. The exemptions from the low flying prohibitions state that 'any aircraft shall be exempt from the 500 feet rule when landing and taking off in accordance with normal aviation practice'. However, a microlight pilot should still ensure they comply with the other low flying requirements, such as not to over-fly a congested area.

It is much easier to get an overall picture of hazards and obstacles when flying over the water than when on it. Distances are also easier to assess from the air. This is very important when it comes to judging your touchdown point and deciding your strategy for taxying/sailing to shore. Remember, your flight has not ended successfully until you are safely at dock with the aircraft securely tethered.

Photo: such a busy area as this is best avoided, but with height one may be able to spot a suitable landing area that would not be evident from lower down.

Another point is that less room is required for landing than for take off. So always bear in mind whether you have sufficient room to get away later. Techniques are available to deal with 'restricted areas' but these are best learned under the supervision of an experienced instructor and not used 'in anger' for the first time having arrived at too small a lake.

Pilots who are familiar with microlight or STOL aircraft will have an advantage over pilots who are only accustomed to landing on prepared surfaces and serviced airfields. The former pilots may indeed have trained at a 'grass strip' and be used to assessing unprepared fields for emergency and planned out-landings. They will have some of the skills required successfully to assess a landing on an unfamiliar stretch of water.

Landing Pattern

Having established where one wants to end up after landing (a mooring area for example), then the area immediately before must be surveyed from the air so that an approach path, landing type, taxy path and mooring plan can be established.

Once it is clear that the mooring, taxying and landing areas are viable (remembering that having landed, any features in the water between the landing area and the docking point will be less visible than from the air) then a pre-landing circuit/approach path can be decided upon, taking into consideration the direction of landing. Unless using an established seaplane base such as at Lake Como in Italy, where a flying circuit is in force (see photo below), then the approach will be largely down to common sense.

Photo: you can just see the line of yellow buoys marking out the water runway at Lake Como, Italy.

Your landing approach should give the best possible view of the landing area and it should avoid built up areas or areas where significant over-flying might cause annoyance (bird sanctuaries for example). Remember you might have to survey the area several times and do a number of go-arounds, before finally committing to the landing. This could - indeed should - take several minutes and it is important to take all the time needed and not rush. The same degree of care should be taken as when making a precautionary out-landing in a field. The establishment of an approach pattern should allow the pilot to form a familiar pattern of behaviour/activity prior to landing, comparable to that in the airfield circuit, which will assist with the discipline of pre-landing procedures such as check lists. In any event, there must never be any rush to land (except maybe in an extreme emergency - and even then check-lists should be followed), especially in unknown and unfamiliar territory.

Once the landing approach/circuit has been established, then a detailed hazard check can be commenced.

Hazards on Landing

One of the additional check-lists associated with seaplanes is the widely-used 'woods' check prior to landing.

- Wind
- Obstacles (surrounding the water)
- Objects (in the water)
- Depth
- Security

Let us take a detailed look at each of these in turn:

Wind

Photos: conditions shown here are calm, but with any wind there is likely to be rotor behind these islands

Landing should normally be into wind and most of the time this option will be available unless operating in a restricted area, for example a narrow waterway. A light crosswind is also acceptable (see the aircraft POH for guidance) providing the water is not rough or the wind turbulent. A tailwind is not normally acceptable, lengthening as it does the landing path and potentially decreasing stability and increasing the tendency of flying boats to porpoise. However, when the wind is so light it is almost impossible to judge, water and air conditions are likely to be so benign that a slight tail wind on landing may not cause a problem (but try to avoid it altogether on a flexwing aircraft).

The difficulty in assessing the wind lies in the fact that around a body of water there may well be an airflow coming from different directions all around the shoreline. This can be caused by small valleys and hills in the vicinity of the lake, or even by tall trees affecting the flow of wind in a particular spot. Another cause may be the air cooling in the evening, sinking and rolling down the land toward the water (a katabatic wind) all around the lake. Equally possible where a large body of water is concerned (including the sea itself of course), sea-breeze conditions can develop whereby the warm air from the land rises up over the colder air over the water, resulting in an on-shore breeze. This may die out and even reverse to a land-breeze later in the day.

We looked at the main wind direction indicators in Chapter 2 and noted that there are many indicators aside from the water itself. However, the water is definitely the best gauge when it comes to gusting conditions. A strong gust produces a distinctive dark patch on the water, usually spreading out downwind of the gust like a hand with outstretched fingers or a 'cat's paw' as they are sometimes known. If these conditions exist then it is vitally important to land the aircraft outside these dark areas, being aware that the gusts could occur at any time before, during and after landing.

These claw-like streaks are distinguishable from much longer, straight streaks (often appearing as white lines due to a topping of froth)... which can appear in a steady wind of 8-10 knots or more. This type of streak usually indicates a strong but steady wind for landing, although the water conditions may be a little choppy. With this type of streak it is often not possible to tell which end is upwind or downwind. However the 'lee' or calm area of water which indicates that the wind is blowing from this side should be clearly visible in this case. Failing that (being too far away from any shore or lee area), fly parallel to the waves and with a strong wind it will be easy to determine which way the wind is blowing from the drift.

As stated earlier, waves and ripples are formed perpendicular to the wind that formed them. The latter part of this sentence is important: 'that formed them'. This may have been a different wind from the one we are going to fly in. Waves do not change direction as soon as the wind does. What tends to happen is that a new pattern of waves emerges with the new wind direction. This superimposes itself on the existing pattern and can cause confusion as to where the wind is really coming from. Other factors then need to be taken into consideration, and as we have said, the most important indicator is the lee area which will react quite quickly to the changing wind.

Note also that the larger the waves created the slower they will be to dissipate and change direction.

It is also important to note that small features such as islands and promontories can affect wind direction in a localised way and also cause turbulence. The lee area immediately behind these features will have calm water but potentially strong air turbulence. Pick your approach and landing spots with care in the vicinity of such areas and be ready to react to turbulence with potentially higher airspeed and less flap, depending on type. Flexwing aircraft should ideally avoid these areas since they may not be able to deal with the sudden turbulence encountered.

Obstacles

This check refers to obstacles on the approach path or close to the intended landing point, such as power lines (whose lines may be almost invisible), tall trees, towers, chimneys, sailing boat masts and flag poles. The area should be surveyed not only for the intended landing path but also for any necessary missed approach scenario.

Photo: obstacles on shoreline such as bridges, pylons and cables. The bridges in the left hand photo are easy to see, but cables, even from a large pylon – such as those in the picture on the right – can be much harder to spot.

As stated earlier, there is even more necessity in a seaplane than a landplane to be 100% happy that the landing will be successful, therefore the possibility of a go-around must always be borne in mind and prepared for. If the desired landing path is suitable, but the missed approach path is not, then a different landing area should be sought. It is a thoroughly undesirable situation to find oneself close to the water, presented with a sudden un-landable situation and no-where else to go. Be particularly careful near islands and archipelagos, where power lines may cross over between the island and the mainland. Look for the poles which support them since these are more easily spotted than the wires themselves.

Objects

Photo: look carefully for objects in the water before landing. These objects may be stationery ....

.... or moving!

A body of water should be checked for objects before every landing. Objects can be either animate or inanimate.   The inanimate ones are usually some kind of floating debris, either on the surface or half-submerged; it also includes buoys, markers and sticks indicating low water and rocks. Shoals are not always marked and one should be careful navigating anywhere on a waterway but especially near a shore or island in case of low water and rocks, sand-bars or objects resting under shallow water.

Animate or moving objects chiefly include swimmers, boats and water fowl. In some areas it may include large water animals. For example, a popular trip when float-flying in Florida is down the Kissimmee River to photograph alligators basking in the sunshine or lying half-submerged in the water. Not the place for an engine failure scenario however.

People are generally very curious about seaplanes and will often try to get a closer look. Apart from getting in your way, they can be at danger themselves from the propeller which they cannot see and may be completely unaware of. Small children in the water may be particularly difficult for you to see (especially in an enclosed cockpit). Be sure you know the 'rules of the road' (see Chapter 7) in case motor boats or other vessels try to get closer. If necessary be ready to abort a take off or landing in the interest of safety: aircraft are not likely to be the winners in any entanglement. Survey the area carefully and keep a mental picture of the number of 'objects' and their relative positions. Remember that wake caused by other water vehicles can also be a danger by causing a large 'swell'. If the swell is parallel to the floats it could cause the aircraft to tip over sidewards; if perpendicular to the floats it can cause severe pitching and again, the possibility of capsize. If the area in question has many such distractions it is advisable to try elsewhere.

Depth

Photo: depth can sometimes be assessed from a good height provided the water is clear. This photo was taken approaching the Isle of Wight, with the Needles in the background.

To some extent we have already covered this in our discussions about surveying the water. Depth is not always easy to assess, even when the water is clear. However if the water is relatively calm, it will be easier to spot rocks and sand-banks lying close to the surface. In choppy conditions this is harder to see. In conditions of medium waves, where there is a distinct wave pattern, a broken or inconsistent portion of wave pattern is likely to indicate the present of rocks or other obstacles just under the surface. Where this is suspected, do not land!

Another consideration is silt which can be deposited at the mouth of rivers flowing into lakes. This can normally be seen from the air but not once on the water.

Photo: river silt, Loch Rannoch, Scotland

In a channel or narrow passage of water, the deepest water is likely to be in the middle. Turbulence or varying wind direction may be experienced from a passage closely bounded by land. In a wider channel or one used by boats and shipping, the safe area is usually marked by buoys and other marks. Where this is not the case, but other vessels are using a passageway, observe their progress closely to find the safe way through.

The use of marine charts may be invaluable in such situations and are to be recommended if use is made of areas used by other water-going vessels. Ordnance Survey maps may also be of some use, at least for distinguishing features around a shoreline, though they will not give water depth, etc.

Security

In general, this check requires that prior to landing safety belts are secure and doors closed. This is the same check that is performed on any normal land plane. However, be aware that the most dangerous moment on the seaplane is probably just after touchdown. This is when the aircraft is most susceptible to unpredicted wind and water conditions. Always be aware, and thoroughly brief any passengers, of the quickest method to release safety belts and exit the aircraft.

Types of Landing

Having now performed the hazards check you can mentally form a picture (or draw a diagram if you have the assistance of a co-pilot) of any obstacles/turn points on the water which will not be visible after landing. If necessary, use features on the shoreline or moored boats etc. to pinpoint your course and turning points during taxying to the mooring area.

The type of landing you make will largely depend on the wind, water and objects/obstacles factors discussed above. Just as on a landplane you may vary your approach and landing according to the strength and direction of the wind, the length and orientation of the runway and other traffic in the pattern, so in a seaplane you will judge the conditions and plan accordingly.

By now, the number of 'variables' in seaplane flying will be abundantly evident with the number one factor being the state of the water. In the previous chapter we discussed the 3 main types of take-off. Correspondingly, there are 3 main types of water landing:

1. Normal Water
2. Glassy Water
3. Rough Water

We will also consider cross-wind and restricted area landings.

Normal Water

Photo: normal water landing - note the waves are perpendicular to the wind

In normal water conditions the aircraft may be landed with or without power, although a power-on landing allows for better control of the aircraft in terms of precision and fast reaction to unexpected events.

The approach should be as for a normal land plane approach, with flaps as recommended by the POH, and aiming to land the aircraft slightly nose up at the lowest possible airspeed. The landing attitude will be about the same, or slightly more nose up, as for taxying on the step. The rear of the floats will touch the water first. Land too fast and you may find that the increase in drag causes the nose to pitch down fast. The elevator must smoothly be brought fully back as the aircraft settles on the water after touchdown and slows. This will keep the nose up and prevent the floats from digging in at the front - an undesirable situation. Once under control on the water perform any after landing checks according to aircraft type and FCARS or equivalent.

Glassy Water

Photo: completely glassy water like this on a cloudy day offers absolutely no clues as to one's height above water. It could even lead you to wonder which way is up!

This is the single most dangerous and deceptive water condition known to the seaplane pilot. Without surface disturbance it is impossible to assess one's height over the water as normal perception is lost. Completely glassy water acts like a mirror reflecting the sky and shorelines. Water may be classed as glassy even if it has faint ripples, caused by the wave patterns of the day subsiding in the evening, for example. Care should be taken when landing even in these conditions, since normal water can give way to glassy water and the pilot needs to change his landing approach accordingly. Very slightly rippled water needs to be treated as glassy. Fading evening light may further exacerbate a situation where the surface is becoming increasingly flat and difficult to make out. If patches of glassy water and normal water co-exist it is preferable to treat the whole area as glassy, to avoid inadvertently arriving over a glassy area without the correct attitude.

Photo: almost mirror conditions at dusk are exacerbated by low light levels, making the landing difficult to judge

The glassy water approach commences with a glide approach and flap set for landing as required. A 'last visual reference point' is selected at which you raise the nose of the aircraft to just above normal landing attitude, equating more or less to the flare attitude of a normal landing. For some types, the precise attitude, rate of descent and target airspeed is stipulated in the POH. Having adopted the attitude, pause to let the airspeed stabilise, then apply enough power to give a constant descent rate of approximately 150 feet per minute (again, check the POH for the precise descent rate). Keep the wings level and aim straight ahead, using peripheral vision if forward vision is obscured by the nose attitude. Expect a long approach. With zero or minimal headwind (hence the glassy water) and power applied, the aircraft will use up a long stretch of water. Keep the attitude resolutely and resist any temptation to judge your height or to anticipate the water. Make any slight adjustments to descent rate/airspeed by varying the power. The aircraft will eventually touch down probably rather later than you expected. Once landing is confirmed (either by spray from the sides or by the sensation of drag from underneath the aircraft) cut the power immediately and bring the elevator fully back as normal. Sometimes it really is difficult to tell that you have landed.

Summary of this technique:

- **P**itch (to correct attitude)
- **P**ause (to stabilise the airspeed)
- **P**ower (to maintain descent rate/airspeed)

There are two ways of attaining the 'last visual reference point' necessary for this type of landing. The one you choose will be largely determined by the terrain. It is useful to practise both methods and therefore to have alternative options in your skills bank.

Landing over a Shore Line

This approach requires that there is a flattish area of land on the approach prior to the water. Make the approach over land, aiming to cross the shoreline edge - which in this case is the 'last visual reference point' - on idle power with as low an altitude as is safely possible. At this point, perform the **PPP** technique: raise the nose to the required attitude, pause to allow the airspeed to settle, and apply power as above. This approach works well when the area surrounding the body of water is free from shoreline obstructions (building, tall trees, etc.).

Landing parallel to the Shore Line

This approach is more suitable where the area around the body of water is steep terrain or there are obstacles, e.g. at lochs and fjords. In this case, it will not be possible to land over the shoreline, so select a distinctive last visual reference point (e.g. a house, marina or land spit) and aim to land along the shoreline, as close to shore as safely possible. The landing attitude and power setting is exactly the same as the previous example and should be selected just as the last visual reference point is reached.

Photo: glassy water approach, parallel to shoreline

Some seaplane pilots advocate throwing objects out of the aircraft in order to make ripples or landing marks on the water, for example small stones or a spare lifejacket. It could then be possible to land on the rippled area or adjacent to the object and retrieve it. In a microlight aircraft the pilot is unlikely to have spare articles on board due to the inherent weight restrictions; nevertheless, this technique could be adopted if such suitable objects were available. However, it is in any case essential to practise the glassy water landing technique as part of a regular flying routine, so that one can use it with confidence if such conditions arise. The technique can be practised at height initially, until one is sufficiently practised at holding the correct attitude and power to try it at low level. Conditions for practice should be suitably calm.

Engine Failure over Glassy Water

There is no definitive advice for this unwelcome scenario, except that you will have to make the best of adopting a glassy water attitude and accept the fact that the lack of power available is likely to result in a harder than ideal touch down. Stay close to the shoreline and choose the parallel approach so that you remain close to shore and watch the shoreline rising. But don't use this as a substitute for a real glassy water approach when the power is still available.

Rough Water

This will always be a powered approach - as opposed to a glide approach - unless you are unlucky enough to have an engine failure.

In an ideal world, rough water conditions are best avoided. 'Cats paws', large numbers of white capped waves and large waves should all make you think again about landing or at least find an area of calmer water. Amphibious aircraft might consider landing on land instead of water, and even some non-amphibious craft might fare better in the relative safety of long grass rather than high waves.

However, if you have no other alternatives, you must find the best area of water that you can, bearing in mind that waves get bigger the further they are downwind. Gusts and turbulent areas are relatively easy to spot and should be avoided as far as possible.

Rough water conditions can vary so much that it is difficult to give a fail-safe approach method. Pitch and power should be coordinated to provide a flattish approach and power is only removed when it is deemed exactly the right moment to land. This should be where the water is least gusty (evidenced by the tell-tale dark patches on the water) so in effect it is a spot-landing. Bouncing can not only damage the aircraft floats and attachments, but also throw the aircraft back into the air without power and at a low airspeed. This could potentially be fatal in a low inertia aircraft. A reduced flap setting may be recommended (see POH) giving a flatter approach, while approach power is retained, maintaining the attitude of the aircraft just prior to landing with forward stick. This allows the pilot the opportunity to power up again quickly and go around or find another landing spot, should the need arise.

Flying boats should ideally be landed on the step in rough water in order to avoid porpoising and then kept on the step to fast taxy to a safe area providing the conditions are not too rough.

You will not wish to stay at the mercy of the rough water longer than is necessary, so aim to land as close to shore as safely possible, being aware that rough water may obscure rocks and other objects. Having landed into wind, in order to avoid step taxying downwind it may be best to cut the power, remain facing into wind and allow the wind to blow you backwards to the nearest shore (using the sailing technique as described in the next chapter). To avoid being blown back hard onto shore or a dock in a high swell you can keep the power on whilst sailing reducing your backwards speed. Needless to say you will wish you had avoided being in this situation. If the direction you land is facing the shore then keep the power and get to shore as quickly as possible.

Should you be unlucky enough to experience an engine failure over rough water, then you have no choice but to carry out a glide approach over the smoothest area you can find and approach with a slightly higher airspeed to give good control close to the water. The danger of getting bounced into the air is quite high so precise pitch control will be paramount. Try to avoid this situation by regarding rough water as a 'no landing option' and therefore remain within gliding distance of better landing areas.

Cross Wind Landings

This will more or less only apply to 'normal' water conditions, since in glassy conditions there will not be enough wind to make a crosswind, and there should not be rough water in an area that is sufficiently restricted to require a cross wind landing. However, it is possible that rough water could exist in a restricted area (where the restricted area is part of a larger body of water that is un-landable due to obstacles for example). In this case, do not land in the restricted area - find somewhere else. In attempting to do so you risk lateral upset of the aircraft as well as damage to the seaplane structure.

Should you need to land in a restricted area with a moderate wind and normal water, care is still required. Your approach will be similar to that in a land plane - using either the crabbed or wing-down method.

Flying boats are better suited to the crabbed approach, rather than wing-down, since there is a danger in the wing-down approach that the wing-float (sponson) could be submerged by the water causing upset. Floatplanes may use either method, but the wing-down approach is preferable since the transition from crabbing to wing down in the latter stages of the approach has to be finely judged and the possibility of incorrect control inputs so close to landing the seaplane are best avoided.

The wing down method, when continued all the way to the water, will result in a one-float landing. The aircraft can then be allowed to settle on both floats after the initial touch-down and the aircraft brought back to idle taxi. If continuing to operate in side-wind conditions after landing the aileron will need to remain into wind and the stick fully back. Note, however, that a single-float operation can be maintained after landing by keeping the aircraft on the landing float and step taxying, using a little less power than normal for step taxying (due to the reduced water drag). This is a useful skill to practise since it could be required in case of a damaged float. A seaplane could be saved from capsize if a holed float can be kept above the water while the aircraft is step-taxied to the shore on the intact float alone.

Compensating for Drift

The unique problem in landing a seaplane crosswind is that you do not have a straight line or runway to follow, with which to assess the offset of drift. You can only use the wavelets as a guide, using sufficient wing-down to stop the relative drift. However, the waves themselves will be flowing downwind, so in stopping perceived drift you will only be countering a portion of the actual drift. You need to counter the 'unseen drift' by using more wing-down than appears necessary. How much extra bank to use is difficult to say, but it is better to overestimate than underestimate. This will almost certainly result in a one-float landing.

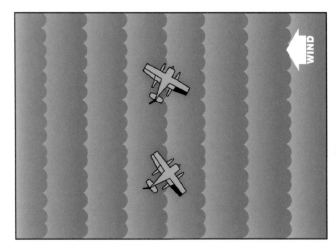

Diagram: the aircraft in front has compensated for the apparent drift using into wind aileron, however, to compensate for 'unseen drift' it may be necessary to bank even further, as the aircraft behind shows.

A flying boat is much more laterally stable on the water than a float-plane, so the problems of crosswind landings are lessened. However, they have one disadvantage which is that their angle of bank is limited due to the sponsons or wing-tip floats which could dig-in to the water if allowed to touch it, causing a yaw towards the wind and possible nose-dive into the water. With these types, the drift should be countered as much as possible without the sponson touching. After landing, the aircraft should be quickly pointed into the wind to stop any un-countered drift causing a downwind yaw and possible burying of the downwind sponson.

Restricted Area Landings

Photo: approaching a small body of water

This applies not so much to narrow bodies of water where a crosswind technique may be necessary (for this, see above) but to smaller bodies of water, e.g. a small lake or bay area. All the normal precautions apply prior to landing and in particular be aware there may be less 'deep' water available. What is classed as a 'small' area is not defined, since it depends not only on the size of the water, but also on the type of aircraft (slower is better), skill and currency of the pilot and the wind conditions. Small bodies of water are likely to have smaller waves.

Assuming you have no option but to land in a restricted area (if it is restricted for landing it may well be impossible for take off) and having performed a thorough 'woods' check, make for the lowest possible safe approach over the shoreline turning as much into wind as possible for landing. An assessment must be made very quickly as to whether the aircraft has sufficient space to carry out the landing.

Photo: this restricted area may also contain obstructions such as bridges and rocky promontories, which can wreck a seaplane.

Post Landing Actions

After a final touchdown the belts should be released and, if expedient on the aircraft in question, the doors opened. Some seaplane pilots use the additional 'HHH' check straight after landing:

- Headsets (off)
- Hatches (open)
- Harnesses (unclipped)

A final FCARS check should now also be performed.

Flexwing Considerations

The pre-landing considerations and types of landing described above apply equally to flexwing types as 3-axis. A normal water landing will be made in much the same way as a landing on land, with a round-out, hold-off and flare. The hold-off is likely to be shorter than on land, due to the increased drag (there is increased drag on a 3-axis seaplane too, but it tends to be even more apparent on flexwing types).

Glassy water conditions pose no additional hazard to flexwing than to 3-axis aircraft. The landing technique is much the same, except that it is the bar held forward which gives the correct landing attitude, as opposed to stick pressure. Power is carried in exactly the same way as on a 3-axis aircraft, the exact amount required depending on type and power plant.

Rough water and cross wind conditions are potentially more hazardous to flexwing types due to the difficulty in controlling the wing in extreme conditions (whilst potentially dealing simultaneously with objects in the water). Rough conditions are always less suitable for smaller, lighter-weight seaplanes and while flexwing aircraft can be very capable in the hands of experienced pilots there is a greater possibility of capsize due to their higher CG than a wheeled version combined with a large wing area. There is also a greater propensity for propeller damage due to their proximity to the water.

In rough conditions you may be advised to tie the wings down laterally to prevent them being exposed to a gust which could blow you over. In a flexwing flying boat, do as the above and if solo, sit in the front of the boat to keep maximum weight forwards and help prevent being tipped over. Keep your weight low to prevent falling overboard and use the paddle to assist getting to shore. Refer back to Chapter 2 for more information about dealing with rough water in a flexwing.

Chapter 5

Mooring and Securing the Aircraft

Photo: be prepared to get wet sometimes. DTA prototype in the south of France.

After landing and taxying to the designated area comes the task of bringing the seaplane safely to a shore or mooring place and securing it there. This can often be a more complex task than simply turning off a runway and taxying to the hangar for parking.

The pathway to the mooring place should have been carefully assessed before landing, as discussed in Chapter 4. If you are landing at a new or previously unknown location then you may not know in advance exactly what mooring options are available. The most common types of mooring are:

1. **Beaching**
2. **Mooring to dock or jetty**
3. **Mooring to a buoy**
4. **Ramping**

Beaching

Photo: Mainair Sprint beached, Thailand.

The approach is made to a prepared or natural beach of sand or small gravel. This must be done bearing in mind the wind, water state and any last minute objects in the water. Ideally the area should be free from other obstacles such as boats, swimmers, etc. The shore or beach should be assessed for trees and obstacles on the shore itself that could catch on the aircraft wings or propeller causing damage. There should be no submerged rocks close to the surface (which may be evident by water breaking in foam over them).

After your full stop landing, you should perform the 'HHH' check: undo harnesses, open hatches and remove headsets. The harness is unfastened so that in the event of a collision and capsize you are free to get out of the aircraft. The hatch (if any) is opened for the same reason, but also so that instructions can be shouted to any helper (or indeed obstructer) on the shore; headsets are removed to assist in the latter.

If the wind is offshore in your docking area you will approach the shore into wind. This means your forward speed will be slowed by the wind allowing you time to review what is happening. Also, the natural weathercocking of the aircraft means that it will remain straight, facing into the wind. Remember you still have no brakes! - so you cannot simply taxy to the shore and stop (although the shore itself will do that for you) for the wind will then start to blow you backwards. It is possible that you will end up in the lee area of the shore without any wind, so in this case you will not be blown back, but the aircraft may be less directionally stable as a result.

Shortly before reaching the beach, be ready with one hand to cut the magnetos, firstly one magneto when still some 10s of metres from the shore - this will slow the aircraft down - and turn off the second magneto just a few metres from the shore. Exactly when to cut the mags is down to practice and will vary according to conditions.

The aircraft will continue to move forwards under its own momentum until it runs out of energy. At this point it may start to move backwards if there is any wind. The idea is to cut the second magneto at just the point when it will have enough forward momentum left to bring it to the shore without crashing into any submerged rocks or other object at the shoreline. If there is a capable assistant waiting to catch the wing or a strut, so much the better. Some 3-axis type aircraft have grab-lines hanging from a wing strut to assist in tying the aircraft to a tree or other suitable object as soon as possible, or at least prevent the aircraft moving away. If this is not practical on the given aircraft type, then the spare grab-line in the cockpit comes in handy. This should be made ready for use when starting the approach to shore. As ever, always be prepared and think ahead. It is no use finding the spare line five minutes after you needed it.

If you have an amphibious aircraft, you may be able to lower the wheels while still in sufficient depth of water that they don't hit the bottom before they are fully lowered (otherwise the lowering mechanism could be badly damaged). Then if the beach area is suitable you can 'drive' up onto dry land. However, the risk of causing damage on an untested surface is fairly high, so only attempt this if you are absolutely certain that the ground is suitable. Additionally, you should raise the water rudder as you arrive in the shallows, in order to prevent damage by rocks or other protrusions.

Photo: warm and wet in Florida.
In a larger seaplane like this you might have room to stow waterproof leggings or Wellingtons.

Be ready to jump out of the aircraft onto a float, or onto the shore itself as soon as the aircraft is close enough. Keep hold of a part of the aircraft as you do so. If you have a passenger make sure they are thoroughly briefed: a well-meaning but unknowledgeable passenger or bystander can damage the aircraft. At a beaching situation as opposed to a dock or jetty, it is likely you will have to step out into the water itself to secure the aircraft so be prepared for this. Secure the aircraft temporarily as quickly as possible while you assess exactly where and how to secure it permanently. The aircraft can be dragged the remaining way onto the beach to stop it from floating around in the water. It is normal to tie both wing struts to an object on either side of the aircraft to make it more stable.

The above has assumed that the aircraft was being manoeuvred into the wind. If the wind is from behind the mags can be cut a little earlier, as the aircraft will in any case be blown onto the shore. In light winds, there should be no problem keeping the aircraft moving downwind but in stronger winds the tendency to weathercock may cause problems. In this case, it may be better to allow the aircraft to weather-cock into the wind and be sailed backwards to the shore. Likewise with a strong cross-wind. The sailing technique is covered further on.

Mooring to a Dock or Jetty

Photo: Seamax being moored to dock. Sometimes you have to improvise: in this example, the low struts of the Seamax means it should be kept from touching the dock itself to avoid possible damage. Floating material is used as an improvised stepping stone for the pilot.

The technique for approaching a fixed dock or jetty is similar to the above, but varies in that one must decide how to present the aircraft to the dock. In other words, should one approach head on, or to one side or other of the dock? This will largely be decided by how the wind is blowing. Also, one should avoid hitting the dock with the aircraft since this can cause damage, so planning the approach is even more important than when beaching. It is better to cut the mags. a little early and face having to restart the engine or paddle to shore, than to crash into the dock and damage a float. Remember, docks are generally built and designed for boats, not seaplanes. Boats don't have wings at an awkward height and are usually well-fendered. Your seaplane, as well as the inconvenience of wings (at this point) and a tail-plane may also have low struts which can easily be damaged by scraping along rocks, posts, poles, and miscellaneous bits of jutting-out metal that are often observed at a jetty. Therefore approach any dock with extreme caution.

The aircraft will need to be moored on one side or other of the dock and which way it faces may be determined by where the door is! In the case of 2 doors or a canopy then this is not an issue, and the pilot in command may prefer to have the dock on the side in which he is sitting. The decision may further be complicated by obstructions (boats, rocks) on one or both sides of the dock.

Photo: a seaplane tied up next to a motor boat.

Either way, the seaplane must be manoeuvred to come alongside the dock at approximately a 45 degree angle to the dock. This angle is so that in the event of any last-minute obstruction or emergency arising, one can turn the aircraft away more easily than if one were approaching head on. Any tendency of the aircraft to be blown back must be countered by swift use of a line to secure the aircraft or some interim measure such as jumping out onto the dock and holding the wing, or using a paddle to hook onto some part of the dock to keep the aircraft temporarily fast. There are usually cleats on the edge of docks to allow boats to be fastened to and these may be used to secure the aircraft. Otherwise, a line tied securely around some other fixed object on the dock can be used.

Wind Direction Considerations at the Dock

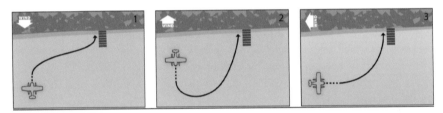

Diagram: different ways to approach a dock with wind from 3 different directions

In picture 1 the wind is blowing from the shore. Landing will be towards the shore and the aircraft can continue to taxy forwards on the step or in idle depending on the circumstances. Cut to one magneto shortly before reaching the dock. The exact approach from then on will depend on other tethered boats or objects at the dock. Assuming the dock is empty, one can continue to taxy on one magneto parallel with the dock and, with sufficient forward momentum to avoid being blown back away from the dock, cut the second magneto while still a few metres away, whilst manoeuvring the aircraft to dock alongside. Never approach nose-onto the dock. Be ready with a tether to prevent being blown backwards away from the dock. In the event of other boats being moored nose onto the dock, the aircraft will have to be turned at right angles to the dock in order to position into an available space. Again, with the wind offshore this will be tricky to negotiate just right and the pilot must be ready if necessary to get out onto a float or open the canopy (in a flying boat) to use lines and paddles as necessary to get the seaplane safely moored.

Should the aircraft be actually blown back from the jetty, the engine may need to be restarted to reposition the aircraft again. Care should be taken doing this when one is already close to the dock and potentially to other onlookers who may have gathered by now. In some cases, it may be preferable to allow the aircraft to be blown back a little further into some clear space before attempting the restart. Use the paddle to dodge objects as necessary.

In picture 2 the wind is offshore. In this scenario the danger will be hitting the dock or shore hard if the aircraft is manoeuvred incorrectly. Cut the magnetos a little earlier and manoeuvre allowing for the wind pushing you past the point where you want to be. At least the aircraft is not going to get away again once it has arrived, however, you don't want to damage the aircraft on arrival either.

In picture 3 the seaplane will land pointing into wind, somewhat to the right of the jetty. You will have to taxy almost right up to the jetty before cutting the second magneto. The aircraft will start to move backwards away from the dock straight away. Shortly before reaching the dock kick the left rudder to turn the aircraft sidewards and be ready with a paddle to grab hold of the dock.

Note that some flying boats are less suitable for mooring to a jetty, since their wings and wing-struts may be too low to avoid collision with the deck. In this case mooring to a buoy or beaching may be more suitable.

Whether floatplane or flying boat, it is always worth testing out the aircraft controls for responsiveness in a clear area before getting too close to the dock, where one may find oneself unable to perform the necessary turns. In this case, sailing may again be the solution.

Mooring to a Buoy

Mooring the aircraft to a buoy is a useful skill, since sometimes there is no safe place ashore. It can also be a useful interim stopping place if, for example, one needs to deal with some item of concern on the aircraft. Usually there is plenty of space around a buoy so the aircraft can be secured and allowed to weathercock into the wind; whether or not the wind is variable in direction the aircraft will not come to any harm.

In order to moor to the buoy a precise assessment must be made of the stopping distance required. The skill to do this successfully is something which can only be acquired with practice. Always approach the buoy into the wind. Use the technique of cutting first one magneto and then the second within a few metres of the buoy. The strength of the wind will dictate how long it takes to stop the aircraft moving forward and send it moving backwards again. The buoy should be approached on the side of the aircraft with the door (if there is only one door) or the side of the pilot in command, so that he can be ready to step onto the float and/or grab the buoy from the aircraft as may be possible in some types. In the case of a twin hull (floatplane), the buoy must never be allowed to pass between the two floats for risk of getting stuck there.

Ramping

Photo: amphibious light aircraft departing the ramp.

A wooden or concrete ramp allows the option of 'driving' the (amphibious) aircraft out of the water onto a safe platform, to keep it clear of the water and allow for easier alighting, inspection and maintenance. It also means the aircraft is on a solid base and not merely tethered in the water where it can drift around.

Some seaplane bases will have such a facility. The wheels can be lowered when there is still plenty of water depth beneath the seaplane to prevent the wheels touching the bottom and damaging the mechanism. This also decreases the speed through the water which can make mooring easier. Approach at idle taxy speed with water rudders down for better directional control. Line up the floats with the centre of the ramp and apply extra power just before contacting the ramp. It may take considerable power to drive up the ramp, which can be a little alarming if you cannot see over the nose of the aircraft or the ramp! Continue to drive up the ramp until onto firm ground where you will hopefully find space to give the aircraft a post-flight check.

In order to depart the ramp, there must be sufficient space to turn the aircraft around and reverse the process. In this case, it should not take much power to get the aircraft moving down the ramp and you can use the brakes to slow it down if necessary. Of course, you will have already surveyed the area and made a plan of action for the likely effect on the seaplane of any prevailing conditions after entering the water. Get ready to lower the water rudder after entering the water to allow good directional control once in the water. Raise the wheels once the aircraft is fully in the water.

Sailing

This is a method of getting from A to B on the water, using the wind to direct your movement. You can only sail backwards, or slightly across the wind. The seaplane can be sailed without power (useful if your engine quit after landing) or on idle power. It is mainly used for manoeuvring into a tight area for docking, where there is insufficient space for a powered turn, or in strong wind conditions where a down-wind taxy is to be avoided. The seaplane will of course weathervane into the wind and be pushed backwards naturally, so in order to manoeuvre to a specific spot to the right or left of the wind line you will have to use the aircraft controls. Generally speaking, you have to point the tail of the aircraft in the direction you want to go: achieve this by using left stick (for example) to raise the left aileron and lower the right aileron, which in turn will catch the wind and cause the nose to turn right, with the tail heading left. Right rudder should be applied which will then assist with the tail turning left. Anything on the aircraft that can catch the wind can also be used to increase the sailing speed, such as flaps and doors, however, the additional effect may be marginal or imperceivable. Water rudders should be up for sailing as they will impede the turning tendency of the seaplane. If you try sailing in a very light wind and away from all fixed objects you may have difficulty seeing your rate of progress, but small floating debris (such as weeds or even foam) should give clues that you are in fact moving. This needs to be practised in an open area to give confidence of trying it in a real situation, on a particular aircraft type.

Anchors

An anchor is a very useful piece of equipment which ideally should be onboard every seaplane, attached to a long length of strong but lightweight line. It should be considered an item of emergency equipment, to be used for example when drifting uncontrollably towards the mouth of a river or onto rocks. In such a case, the anchor should be carefully lowered over the side (not thrown recklessly) until it bites onto the water bed. Needless to say, the other end of the line must be securely fastened within the aircraft. The whole thing must also be within easy reach, behind or underneath the pilot's seat.

Securing the Aircraft

Always be ready to secure the aircraft with a spare grab-line when coming to shore. The line should be neatly coiled when not in use and arranged in such a way that it can quickly be uncoiled and put to good use. Firstly, be sure that the aircraft will not be damaged by contact with the shore, jetty, rocks, boats or protrusions on the shore itself, e.g. flagpoles, masts. All contact should be slow and gentle. If space permits, a fender could be carried aboard the aircraft for this purpose, although most small seaplanes will not accommodate this. Have the line ready to attach one end to a strut or other suitable part of the aircraft, and the other to an available metal hoop or cleat on the shore ... or around a rock, tree or other suitable item.

Photo: getting ready to dock. In this flexwing flying boat (Polaris FIB) the pilot or passenger can stand ready to grab the mooring or fend off the plane from rocks or other objects at the shoreline and tie it securely. In twin-float aircraft, it is possible to get out onto a float to prepare for docking (assuming someone is still at the controls!)

Once the aircraft is safely tethered the local wind situation and its likely effect on the tethered aircraft can be assessed. At that point the aircraft can be fastened in an appropriate fashion to its mooring.

It is useful to know a few knots for various situations. It is not necessary to know the full range of knots available, but learn and practise about 4 or 5, so that you can deal with almost any tethering situation. A few of the most useful and versatile knots are listed in Appendix B.

In the case of amphibious aircraft, landing at an airfield or at least, on dry land, it is still necessary to secure the aircraft after flight. Most floatplanes are higher than a normal landplane due to their floats and the addition of wheels to this can add a significant height to the aircraft. This raises the CG somewhat and can make the aircraft more susceptible to being blown over in a strong wind or sudden squall. Flexwing aircraft should be parked with the wing tied down against the wind wherever possible.

Keeping the Line Tidy

Ropes on a boat are always referred to as 'lines'. Different lines can have different names to distinguish them; a beginner's marine handbook will help you to avoid using the wrong terms.

The most important thing on the seaplane is to keep the lines tidy and handy. Remember, a long length of rope can weigh considerably (even more so when wet) so don't keep more than necessary on board, and try to find lightweight nylon line. It is good seamanship to keep lines nicely coiled. One method is as follows:

Firstly, since most lines are 'right hand laid', always coil the line clockwise to prevent them forming a figure of 8.

1. Coil the line as many times as required (a forearm's length is a good rule of thumb), then wrap the free end around the coil two or three times, near the head, to keep it from unravelling.
2. Put the free end through the eye thus made at the head and push it back through the same eye to form a small loop.
3. Push the loop over the head of the coil.
4. Feed the 'bitter end' (the end used to make the knot) through this loop in order to secure the bundle. This keeps the line neat and ready for immediate use.

Flexwing Considerations

All of the mooring options available for a 3-axis aircraft are also available for a flexwing seaplane. In fact the open structure of a flexwing aircraft means that some of the practical aspects of mooring and docking are that much easier, for example, there are no doors to open or canopy to release. It should therefore be easier and quicker to grab hold of a dock and attach a line to mooring cleat, for example. However, the relatively poorer stability of a flexwing seaplane means that such operations must be carried out with care, to avoid tilting or upsetting the aircraft at the dock, especially when exiting the aircraft. Keep your weight low in the aircraft and clamber around inside a flying boat hull with care. There are plenty of lines, cleats and blocks onboard which are exposed and can easily be tripped over.

Control of the wing remains of paramount importance, so don't forget to keep an eye on this at all times. The wing being moveable, it can either be affected by the wind or easily snagged on objects at the jetty. Hopefully the dock will be a sheltered area but there can still be plenty of hazards waiting. One of these may be unwary on-lookers. Make sure they keep clear of the wings (so they don't risk being knocked into the water) and away from the propeller area at all times.

Photo: a flexwing flying boat moored to a buoy from the bow and stabilised with a line from the stern - presumably to shore. If the stern line were unavailable, the use of a drogue anchor could be considered here to keep the bow pointing into the wind.

Note that a flexwing seaplane can be sailed backwards, using the large wing area to catch the wind and push it to the right or left of straight downwind. This can be useful if the engine quit or to manoeuvre in light winds and tight areas. However, sailing a flexwing backwards is still very prone to the hazards of having the wings snag as you approach a dock and in any case you have to be very proficient at moving the wing at the right time and to the right extent, possibly over quite a long period of time on the water. If this all gets too exhausting it might be better to tie the wings down on each side and start paddling.

Chapter 6

Emergency Procedures
- Capsize & Recovery

Photo: stricken Quicksilver, Clearwater, Florida

Causes of Capsize & Immediate Actions

What can cause a seaplane to capsize? We have alluded to some of the possible causes in passing. The most likely of these include:

- an unrecognised glassy water condition causing a mis-timed flare and subsequent heavy 'splashdown'.
- step-taxying from downwind to upwind.
- failing to check the landing gear is up when landing an amphibian on water.
- too short a take off or landing run available, resulting in misuse of the controls as the pilot tries to avoid a rapidly advancing shoreline - resulting in a stall and heavy landing.

These and many other circumstances can cause the aircraft to land heavily or land with the floats nose down or sideways, leading to the subsequent capsize of the aircraft.

If an aircraft is rolled over on land, statistics show you will probably walk away with only minor damage to yourself and repairable damage to the aircraft. Your mates will turn up and help you remove the damaged aircraft to a hangar in remarkably quick time.

Capsize an aircraft on water and the problems are compounded. The initial capsize may not damage the aircraft at all - water is softer than land, at least at low speeds - so all you will have is an upside down craft: embarrassing but recoverable. However it is the ensuing actions that will determine the gravity of the situation that follows.

Firstly, it is vital that passengers are briefed on what to do in the event of capsize before it happens. Dealing with a stricken aircraft, inconvenient and embarrassing though it may be, pales into insignificance compared to dealing with loss of life, especially when this is usually preventable. Life jackets are of little use thrown into the back of the aircraft for 'emergency purposes'. If they are not worn it is unlikely there will be time to get them on in case of such an outcome. Passengers must also be shown how to release their harnesses quickly and without panic and how to open the cockpit doors or hatch. Force may be required as the aircraft fills with water and it may be necessary to wait until the pressure equalizes on the inside of the aircraft before the door can be released. DO NOT inflate life jackets until you are outside the aircraft cabin.

Once outside, it is normally best to remain with the aircraft, assuming it is floating. Help will surely come, and it is much better to wait for it than risk trying to swim for the shore (which is always further than it looks). Additionally, swimming in a cold lake or, worse still, the sea is a far different proposition from swimming in your local swimming pool. Even strong swimmers have been known to come to grief when trying to get to shore after a boat has capsized. The exception to this rule is when there is a leakage of fuel and oil which, lying on the water surface, could present a fire hazard. Since the engine will be submerged, there is little chance of this actually happening. In case there appears to be any danger of this, after inflating life jackets swim upwind from the aircraft and await help at a safe distance.

Most likely the capsize of an aircraft will be spotted by another water-user who will raise the alarm. However, rather than relying on this, it might be advisable to have a water-proof means of communication on board at all times. This could be a spare radio and/or mobile phone in a water-tight container strapped to the pilot in command at all times. This could be invaluable when flying late in the evening or in remote areas. Check out marine suppliers for suitable water-tight equipment.

Aircraft Recovery

Once rescued, you will have to find the means to recover the stricken aircraft. This will depend on where it capsized and what type it is.

Most damage to the seaplane is usually caused during the rescue rather than the accident itself. An unknowledgeable retrieve crew can cause considerable damage if they are not careful with their handling. Since seaplanes are relatively rare it is unlikely you will find an experienced seaplane rescue crew just when you need one and instead you will have to make do with a diver, a water based vehicle and a land based vehicle, ideally with a hoisting device. Assume your crew know nothing about seaplanes and prepare to supervise the rescue closely.

There are some things you can do to minimize damage. Firstly, if your aircraft has capsized in salt water, then the damaging effect of corrosion will not begin until it is subjected to oxygen, i.e. in the air. So if the accident occurs in the evening it is better to leave the aircraft in the water overnight. Once it is taken out of the water it is necessary to take anti-corrosive measures as quickly as possible.

Floatplanes will normally float on the surface after capsize. The large float areas keep them suspended more or less at the water surface level. A disadvantage of the flying boat type is that, if holed, it does not have sealed compartments to prevent further ingress of water. Theoretically the whole boat could fill with water and cause it to sink leaving no surface trace.

One Method of Recovery

Generally speaking, and assuming the aircraft is not too far below the surface, a line will have to be attached from a rescue boat or vehicle to slowly and gently drag the aircraft close to the shore. A diver accompanying the aircraft underwater can assist to ensure the aircraft does not impact hard on any underwater objects or rocks.

The aircraft should be raised by a crane out of the water bit by bit, nose first, until fully vertical, allowing it to drain at each stage and bilging each float compartment (in the case of a floatplane) as they emerge from the water. Once the tail is clear, a line can be attached to the tail to bring it back to the upright position.

In the event that a crane is not available, the aircraft should be dragged as close to shore as possible, leaving a depth of water below equivalent to just more than the length of the aircraft. With the nose of the aircraft facing the shore, the front floats can be holed with a drill, allowing them to fill with water and sink. The aircraft can then be eased tail over nose and dragged gently to shore from the tail end. Close supervision should minimise the damage caused, though total prevention is unlikely. Once dragged clear of the water, the holed floats can be pumped out and eventually repaired.

Alternate Method of Recovery:

If you happen to have a friendly helicopter pilot on-hand, a variation on the above recovery method is possible. See the sequence of photos below which track the recovery of a quicksilver floatplane:

Photo 1: spot the floatplane. The windsurfer is an on-looker.

Photo 2: a winch is attached to the floats' spreader bar and the aircraft is slowly pulled upwards, assisted by a diver.

Photo 3: handy to have a helicopter on stand-by. The floatplane is pulled clear of the water.

Photo 4: the floatplane is lowered to land, with ground assistance.

Photo 5: amazingly, the aircraft was back in operation the same day.

Whatever the method of recovery, the aircraft must immediately be washed down (if in salt water) and anti-corrosion protected. Any delay in this will greatly increase the damage done. Engines vary in complexity, and the severity of the damage will depend on the engine type. Generally speaking, the engine must be removed, drained of all fluids, washed extremely thoroughly and new fluids added. It should be started up again as soon as possible. It would be wise to get it thoroughly checked by an expert.

Any electronic instruments may suffer extreme damage and be unusable, even after a brief time in the water. Remove them, wash in fresh water and dry them off in a very low oven or bright sunshine as quickly as possible, then check whether they are usable. Send them to an expert repair shop for a thorough check and overhaul.

Damaged Float or Hull

With regard to damaged floats and hulls, most fibreglass damage can be successfully repaired. Metal-hulled aircraft will need to have each damaged metal panel replaced.

Most floats leak a little, as it is almost impossible to produce a completely water-tight float chamber. Rivets and joins are the culprits, since these are stretched and distorted by constant water pounding. Pumping out the floats is part of the pre-flight check requirement, and this should be done religiously. If more and more water is found in any compartment, then it is an indication that a small leak is becoming worse. Efforts should be made to find the leak (possibly by filling the compartment with water and seeing where it comes out) and repairs made.

However, it is possible that a leak may occur during a particular flight - or more likely landing or taxy session - which may cause a more sudden and severe leak to occur. If this causes just one compartment to flood then the damage is contained and although the degrade in performance will be noticeable - difficulty climbing onto the step, excessively long take-off run or floats low in the water - it should still be possible to get the aircraft flying or taxy to a safe shore to investigate the cause. It may be possible to perform a single-float high speed taxy in the event of evident damage in just one float.

If the problem is allowed to compound such that the aircraft may no longer be able to take off, or is very low in the water indicating a sinking possibility, then steps must immediately be taken to get the aircraft to a safe shore or land base. If takeoff is still possible then this may be attempted but only if the controls are still manageable. Unfortunately, one cannot be sure of this until the aircraft is airborne, which is not a safe time to find out. In this event, after take off treat the aircraft very gently and do not make any large control deflections or steep turns. Do not attempt taking off at all in restricted areas, areas of mechanical turbulence or in strong thermic conditions.

Having taken off, landing on land (preferably on long, damp grass) - even on a non-amphibious type - should be considered as an alternative to putting the aircraft back in the water. Most seaplanes can be landed safely on land (although you will find it rather harder to take off again!). It is certainly preferable to risking a sunken aircraft.

Finally - it may seem impossible to sink a floatplane that has compartmentalized floats (as all modern floatplanes have) - nevertheless, instances have occurred.

Amphibious Considerations on Land

It is not just on water that one needs to take care of a seaplane. Amphibious floatplanes can be quite 'tall' and their higher than normal centre of gravity makes them more susceptible to gusty conditions when on land. This is particularly true of the lighter-weight seaplanes which obviously carry more risk in a strong wind, but the risk is by no means limited to these. See the photo below. This amphibious floatplane blew over on the runway.

Photo: it's not safe until it's back in the hangar. Luckily no occupants were hurt.

Other Emergency Situations
– Engine or Cabin Fire

Engine fire or cabin fires in the air should be treated as one treats a land plane in such a situation. The bonus in a seaplane is that there is a large fire extinguisher right underneath! Get down on water as fast as it is safe to do so and having brought the aircraft under control exit as expediently as possible, preferably upwind of the fire to avoid the fumes. Make sure you are also clear of any surface leakage of fuel.

Forced Landing over Land - Non Amphibians

With straight floats or a flying boat hull it is perfectly possible to land safely on land. The ideal landing place is a large flat area of long damp grass. Since this ideal is rarely available at short notice, make a point of surveying landing areas when flying out of range of water and always consider your landing options.

Flexwing Considerations

In the case of damage to floats or hull, the same actions should be taken as described above. The flexwing type has an advantage in having an open cockpit, so there are no hatches/doors to open. However, in a capsize situation this means that one's exit into the water is rapid and immediate! All the more reason to be quick about unclipping the harness and the jettison of headsets and helmets.

This sequence of photos shows a flexwing flying boat after a poorly executed landing (right wing is lifting) and the subsequent tipping over of the boat. Largely due to the sea-worthiness of the rubber hull, the boat remained only partially capsized and the wing stayed above the surface.

In terms of aircraft recovery, the procedure is similar to that described above. The large wing will create considerable drag when attempting to upright the aircraft and extra care must be taken not to exert undue force on it during the recovery. The A-frame must be securely tied town to prevent movement and damage during the operation. You will need a reasonably large motor boat positioned alongside the capsized aircraft. A diver should attach a line from the boat to the underwater kingpost and then apply his weight to the aft of the hull/floats, such that when the boat moves away from the aircraft, the aft of the boat is forced downwards by the diver's weight and the kingpost is pulled upwards. As the aircraft is slowly flipped over and the wing emerges from the water, the diver can transfer his weight from the aft to the bow to assist in pulling the aircraft back to the upright position.

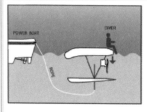

6.

Diagram: flexwing recovery in 3 stages. 1: line attached to power boat, diver ready. 2: power boat pulls aircraft upright. 3: diver guides nose of boat to upright position.

The engine and instruments will need anti-corrosion treatment as above and the wing will need to be carefully inspected for force or damage. Particularly in a salt water situation, the whole wing will need to be stripped down and all of the tubing carefully washed and treated.

Chapter 7

Seaplane Rating and Theory

Seaplane Rating

At the time of writing, a seaplane rating may be added either to a microlight or a light aircraft licence (NPPL SSEA or JAR SEP). A light aircraft pilot can obtain a light aircraft seaplane rating, or can obtain a microlight seaplane rating if he first obtains an NPPL(M). A microlight pilot may of course only add a microlight seaplane rating to his licence: NPPL(M) or its predecessor (microlight PPL).

In the case of a microlight, the applicant must be type-rated or have signed-off differences training on the type of aircraft to be used for the seaplane rating (for example, if the applicant is type rated on flexwing microlights and not signed-off on 3-axis, then the sea rating must be conducted on a flexwing seaplane).

Minimum seaplane training requirements:

- Complete five hours of dual training with a seaplane instructor
- Pass a General Skill Test (GST) with seaplane examiner
- Pass an Oral Test (Technical)
- Pass a written Seamanship exam (multiple choice questions)

The above is the same for both microlights and light aircraft.

Syllabus

The syllabus covers the following aspects of flying:

- Aircraft familiarisation and preparation for flight
- Starting up
- Departure from the dock considerations
- Taxying techniques
- Normal water take off and climb
- General handling (familiarisation on type)

- Normal water approach and landing
- Glassy water take off and landing
- Rough water take off and landing
- Mooring, docking, beaching, ramping, sailing
- Emergency operations

The five hours of dual training is a minimum requirement and this may well be exceeded. There is no requirement to fly solo. The training must cover all aspects of the exercises in the syllabus listed above, subject to local training environment (for example, a ramp may not be available). The GST may comprise one or two separate flights. Normally, the oral test will be taken around the same time as the GST and in the proximity of the aircraft itself, so that aspects of the aircraft structure and components may more easily be discussed.

The application must be made within 12 months of passing the written test and within 9 months of passing the GST. Once issued, the sea rating can then be re-validated within its validity period by completing the requisite number of hours to keep the licence valid (12 hours in a light aircraft, 5 hours in a microlight) to include at least 1 hour of seaplane flying and 12 takeoffs and landings on water. The exact requirements are detailed in LASORS (only for SEP ratings at the time of writing).

We have dealt with the practical aspects of seaplane flying in the preceding six chapters, so now to the theoretical knowledge requirements. This can be broadly divided into the following topics:

1. **The Rules of the Road**
2. **Buoys and Buoyage**
3. **Symbols and Abbreviations used on Admiralty Charts**
4. **Tides**
5. **Lights required on Seaplanes**

1. Rules of the Road

In total there are 37 Rules of the Road published in their entirety by the International Maritime Organization (IMO) in their 'International Conference on the Revision of the International Regulations for Preventing Collisions at Sea, 1972', which can usefully be shortened to 'Rules of the Road', 'Collision Regulations' or simply 'Colregs'.

The book 'A Small Boat Guide to the Rules of the Road' by John Mellor helps to explain the rules with examples and diagrams. As the title suggests, it is primarily aimed at the small boat owner, so although the book is in the recommended reading list for the seaplane course, what follows here is a summary of the key Colregs from a seaplane pilot's perspective.

The Colregs are divided into four 'parts' as follows:

- **Part A   General**
- **Part B   Steering and Sailing Rules**
- **Part C   Lights and Shapes**
- **Part D   Sound and Light Signals**

Part A - General

This Part puts the Rules which are to follow in context, by explaining to whom they apply, responsibilities of seagoing vessels and some general definitions.

Rule 1a states that the rules are applicable 'to all vessels **upon the high seas** and in **all waters connected therewith** navigable by seagoing vessels'. This means that seaplanes operating on the sea and its connecting channels, rivers and estuaries are bound by the Rules. It does not mention land-locked bodies of water, e.g. lakes and lochs, so it is important to realise that these types of water are not covered by the Rules and will likely have their own local regulations, administered by a landowner or water regulation body.

Rule 1b states that 'nothing … shall interfere with the operation of **special rules** made by an appropriate authority', meaning that local waterway authorities/harbour masters may make their own additional rules, though they should follow the Rules of the Road as closely as possible.

Rule 2 (Responsibility) states that 'nothing … shall exonerate any vessel … from the consequences of **any neglect to comply with these Rules or of the neglect of any precaution which may be required by the ordinary practice of seamen**'. For the seaplane pilot, this means that you are required to comply with the Rules UNLESS circumstances dictate that you have to depart from the Rules for the safety of your seaplane. In other words, common sense should prevail and the sea-going captain should always bear this in mind and assess the circumstances in which he is 'playing by the Rules'. Part b of this Rule goes on to state explicitly that there are circumstances which 'may make a departure from these Rules necessary to avoid immediate danger'.

Rule 3 gives definitions and terms which are important since they are used in later Rules. Part a clarifies that the word 'vessel' (in Rule 1a) 'includes every description of water craft, including ... seaplanes' whilst Part e qualifies this by saying a seaplane 'includes any aircraft designed to manoeuvre on the water'.

A seaplane is subject to the terms used to describe a vessel's situation on the water which include **'underway'** meaning that it is 'not at anchor, or made fast to the shore, or aground' (i.e. it is on the water but not moving through it) and should be distinguished from **'making way'** which means it is moving (forwards) through the water (as opposed to 'making stern way' which is the reverse).

Other important definitions include **'vessel not under command'** - which does not mean that no-one is on board - but does mean it is 'unable to manoeuvre (in order to comply with the Colregs) ... and is therefore unable to keep out of the way of another vessel' and **'power-driven vessel'** which means any vessel 'propelled by machinery' (i.e. an engine, but also includes sailing vessels which are moving under power and not by sail alone).

Part B - Steering and Sailing Rules

This Part is further divided into three sections:

- **Section 1: conduct of vessels in any visibility**
- **Section 2: conduct of vessels in sight of one another**
- **Section 3: conduct of vessels in restricted visibility**

Section 1

This section contains Rules 4-10 which are general rules to avoid getting into collision situations. This section contains important Rules for the seaplane which are discussed below:

Rule 4 states that rules in this section apply in any **condition of visibility** (even completely clear conditions)

Rule 5 'Look Out' - states that every vessel must maintain a **'proper look-out by sight and hearing'** and by other means as appropriate. A good look-out should already be second nature to the airplane pilot, but this is a reminder that the look-out must continue when on the water itself where in fact there may be more traffic than in the air. Also some vessels may make signals by sound, so 'listening out' is equally important. Sailors and captains of sea-going vessels may use binoculars to spot other vessels, but the seaplane pilot may not have these on board and is therefore restricted to good eyesight and vigilance.

Rule 6 'Safe Speed' - states that a vessel must **'proceed at a safe speed so that she can take proper and effective action to avoid collision'** within the prevailing circumstances. These circumstances may include visibility, traffic density, manoeuvrability, and wind and sea state, among others listed in the Rule.

Rule 7 'Risk of Collision' - states that the vessel shall do everything within its means to determine whether a risk of collision exists and **'if there is any doubt such risk shall be deemed to exist'**. In other words, err on the side of caution.

Rule 8 'Action to avoid Collision' very importantly states that if such action is taken it must 'be **positive**, made in **ample time** and with due regard to the **observance of good seamanship'**. It further goes on to say that such action should be 'large enough to be readily apparent to another vessel ...; **a succession of small alterations of course and/or speed should be avoided'**. In other words it is no use making a change of course/speed which is only detectable to yourself, since the other vessel would not be aware of your intentions. You must make it clear to the other vessel that you have seen them and that you ARE taking action. This may require a large change in speed combined with a clear change of course (probably in excess of that required to avoid the collision, but sufficient to show the intention). The point is to remove the uncertainty of the situation for both (or all) vessels involved. Section 2 of Part B gives further information about specific avoiding action.

Rule 9 'Narrow Channels' deals with several aspects of passing through a narrow waterway including that the vessel should **'keep as near to the outer limit of the channel ... which lies on her starboard side as is safe and practicable'**. So no taxying selfishly straight down the middle. Obviously, the depth of water in the channel has a part to play, but a small vessel is less constrained than a large vessel. The Rule specifically states that 'a vessel of less than 20 metres in length ... shall **not impede the passage of a vessel which can safely navigate only within a narrow channel'**. The message here is to be aware of the restrictions of larger or more restricted vessels and give way accordingly. Note that certain sound signals apply to operating in a narrow channel in regard to crossing/overtaking another vessel. Therefore if you intend to perform such manoeuvres you should be in possession of a suitable sound-making device (whistle or bicycle horn, for example) and also be aware of sound signals made by other vessels. Hopefully your headsets will be off at this point!

Rule 10: 'Traffic Separation Schemes' (TSS) provides some general common sense guidance for the correct procedures when using these schemes and points out that when in a TSS one is not exempted from other Rules. A TSS is generally established in a very busy shipping area, such that one may well be advised to avoid it altogether in a small and vulnerable seaplane. As well as the need to **'proceed in the appropriate traffic lane in the general direction of traffic flow'** and observe other rules regarding safety and good seamanship, a vessel should as far as possible 'avoid crossing traffic lanes, but if obliged to do so **shall cross on a heading as nearly as practicable at right angles to the general direction of traffic flow'.**

Section 2

This section contains Rules 11-18 and is concerned with specific actions required of vessels that are in a potential collision situation. The vessels must be in visual sight of one another.

The important Rules for seaplanes are:

Rule 13 'Overtaking' defines overtaking as approaching another vessel **'from a direction more than 22.5 degrees abaft her beam'**. This means more than a quarter of the way (22.5 degrees) from abeam the vessel to the aft of the vessel. This may not be terribly clear in daylight and would be more easily recognised at night, when the aft light would shine from 22.5 degrees abaft the beam on both sides. Therefore if you were in this aft-light arc (and the faster vessel) you would be in an 'overtaking' situation. In daylight, you have to err on the side of caution by assuming you are in the overtaking situation and acting accordingly. This means, among other things, **keeping well clear of the other vessel** until 'finally past and clear'.

Rule 14 'Head on Situation' applies when 'two power-driven vessels are **meeting on reciprocal or nearly reciprocal courses'** and they shall each 'alter **her course to starboard'.** Again the Rule requires that the existence of doubt obliges the pilot to act as though in a collision situation. Note that the Rule applies when 'on a reciprocal or nearly reciprocal course' which means that the doubt element can be eliminated early by means of action as though the vessels are actually head on. This is to avoid uncertainty and a delay in taking avoiding action.

Rule 15 'Crossing Situation' states simply that 'the vessel which has the other on her own starboard side **shall keep out of the way and shall .... avoid crossing ahead** of the other vessel'. This is similar to the rule familiar to pilots and needs no further explanation.

Rule 16 'Action by give-way Vessel' is similarly succinct in its requirement for the vessel giving way to **'take early and substantive action to keep well clear'**.

Rule 17 'Action by stand-on Vessel' should be familiar to pilots with the notion that the vessel 'in the right' should **'keep her course and speed'**. However common sense comes into play in allowing the vessel to take avoiding action in case it is not clear that the other vessel is doing so. The vessel giving way must also keep well clear of the other vessel.

Rule 18 'Responsibilities between Vessels' defines the 'pecking order' of vessels on the water in terms of their right of way over each other. The list is as follows, together with the shorthand abbreviation for each type plus a standard mnemonic. Each vessel has to give way to any vessel higher up the list.

Description of Vessel	Shorthand	Mnemonic
Vessel not under command	NUC	Nuclear
Vessel restricted in her ability to manoeuvre	RESTRICTED	Restrictions
Vessel constrained by her draft	CONSTRAINED	Constrain
Vessel engaged in fishing	FISHING	Fishing (and)
Sailing vessel	SAILING	Sailing
Power-driven vessel underway	POWER	People
Seaplane	SEAPLANE	Say

Note where the seaplane lies! However, the rule goes on to say that 'a seaplane on the water shall, in general, keep well clear of all vessels and avoid impeding their navigation. In circumstances, however, where risk of collision exists, she shall comply with the Rules'.

In other words, a seaplane can go about her business on the water as long as she does not get in the way of other vessels. In the case of a collision risk, the rights of way shown above must be observed.

Section 3

This relates to the conduct of vessels in restricted visibility (e.g. fog).

The section is limited to Rule 19, which states that vessels operating in conditions of limited visibility shall do so with utmost care. Since these are conditions where a seaplane is unlikely to be taxying, taking off or landing you need only be aware that the Rule exists and any vessel operating on the water should 'navigate with extreme caution' and be ready to manoeuvre under power to avoid another.

Part C - Lights and Shapes

This Part contains Rules 20-31 and concerns itself with lights and shapes which indicate the type of vessel and the bearing of that vessel towards another vessel. Shapes are generally an alternative to lights and may be displayed by day, but obviously only lights are visible at night.

Rule 20 'Application' tells us that what follows applies in all weather conditions; that **Rules concerning lights apply from sunset to sunrise** and in 'all other circumstances when it is deemed necessary' and that Rules regarding shapes are to be complied with during the day.

Rule 21 'Definitions' goes on to define the different **type of lights and their position** on the boat; these definitions include Masthead light, Sidelights, Stern light, Towing light, All-round light and Flashing light.

Rule 22 'Visibility of Lights' gives the minimum ranges at which the lights should be visible.

Rule 23 'Power-driven vessels underway' states the lights to be displayed by this type of vessel, which includes seaplanes. Note that the minimum requirement for the smallest vessel (less than 7 metres in length and with a speed of less than 7 knots) is reduced to **'an all-round white light'** with sidelights as an option 'if practicable'. Note that the option to display merely one white all-round light on a small seaplane does not exonerate the pilot from being able to recognise the lights of other vessels around him. Also, be aware that due to the nautical sunset rule being exactly from sunset until sunrise, it would be possible to land a seaplane within the 30 minutes after sunset perfectly legally according to aviation law, but then to find oneself taxying without an all-round light and therefore illegally according to the Colregs for boats.

Rules 24, 25, 26, 28 and 29 have no relevance for seaplanes, though it may be useful to have read them.

Rule 27 concerns those vessels which are 'not under command' or are restricted in their ability to manoeuvre. This could include a seaplane on the water with an engine failure for example. In this case, note that if less than 12 meters long you are not obliged to show any lights or shapes. Similarly Rule 30 concerns 'Anchored vessels and vessels aground' - which could include a seaplane aground - however, there is a similar exemption for vessels less than 12 meters.

Finally, **Rule 31** 'Seaplanes' is as follows: 'where it is impracticable for a seaplane to exhibit lights and shapes of the characteristics or in the positions prescribed in the Rules of this Part she shall exhibit lights and shapes **as closely similar in characteristics and position as is possible**'. In other words, do your best.

Part D - Sound and Light Signals

Rule 32 'Definitions' gives the definitions of the terms 'whistle', 'short blast' and 'long blast'.

Rule 33 'Equipment for sound signals' states what sound-making equipment can be used and also states that a vessel of less than 12 metres in length is exempted from the prescribed equipment, but should carry **'some other means of making an efficient sound signal'**. This implies that at least a whistle should be carried and also that one knows the correct sound signals to make.

Rule 34 'Manoeuvring and warning signals' lists the sound signals that may be used in different circumstances. Rule 35 defines 'Sound signals to be used in restricted visibility' while Rule 36 defines 'Signals to attract attention' which could be any signal as long as it could not be mistaken for any of the other defined signals.

Finally, **Rule 37** 'Distress Signals' states that specific signals should be used for indicating grave distress and urgent assistance required. These are worth memorising and are as follows:

1. Gun or explosive signal fired about once a minute
2. Continuous sounding of foghorn
3. Rockets/shells firing single red stars at short intervals
4. Morse SOS made by any means
5. A MAYDAY call by telephone or radio
6. International code flags N above C

7. A square flag and a round shape hoisted together
8. Flames on a vessel (e.g. a burning rag on a boathook)
9. Red flares
10. Orange smoke
11. Slow, repeated raising and lowering of outstretched arms
12. Built-in alarm signals from radio transmitters
13. Signals from Emergency Position Indicating Radio Beacons (EPIRBs)
14. Approved signals from radio transmitters

Additionally the following signals are for identification from the air:

1. Orange canvas marked with black square and circle
2. Dye marker

Whilst is may be unlikely that a small seaplane will be carrying the majority of the above signal makers, thought should be given to those that could easily be included in the 'emergency gear to hand' that we discussed in an earlier chapter. Even on a weight-restricted microlight these could easily include a spare telephone or radio in a water tight container, the flags N and C, flares and an EPIRB. Also, as a seaplane pilot one has the unique advantage of being able to survey an area from the air, so be aware of emergencies aboard other vessels and be ready to give assistance by reporting the position of any vessel seen to be exhibiting distress signals.

So much for the Rules of the Road. If all of the above sounds a bit daunting remember that most of it is logical common-sense. However, if you are intending to operate your seaplane in a marine environment it is vital that you know and can comply with the Colregs. Not to do so would be the equivalent of arriving at a busy airfield without having PPR, no knowledge of circuit procedures and bad RT. You would be a danger to yourself and other pilots and would be made most unwelcome, if not actually prosecuted. The best advice is to study the above carefully and also become acquainted more with the marine environment from a mariner's perspective: buy a beginner's sailing book; join the local boat club; offer a flight in your aircraft in exchange for some sailing experience; or even do a yacht-master's course. It will stand you in very good stead to be as competent on the water as you aim to be in the air.

2. Buoys and Buoyage

Photo: runway marker buoy, Lake Como

The theoretical knowledge on the buoyage system required for the seaplane rating is contained within the International Association of Lighthouse Authorities (IALA) publication: the 'IALA Maritime Buoyage System'. This fearsome sounding title is in fact a slender but vital work published by the Hydrographic Office. It is essential reading for the theory exam for the seaplane rating.

The publication starts with an introduction explaining how the current system for marking waterways has its roots in the 19th century. Several different systems developed in different regions of the world before IALA succeeded in getting world-wide agreement for just 2 alternative systems to be adopted worldwide. This has given us the 'Region A and Region B' systems, whereby Region A applies to Europe, Africa, Australia and parts of Asia, and Region B applies to the Americas and the remainder of Asia. Since we are dealing with a UK seaplane rating, it is Region A on which we should focus.

The introduction continues with definitions of the Marks (or buoys), Colours, Shapes, Topmarks, Lights and Reflectors used in the system.

The publication goes on to discuss, with explanations and diagrams, the buoyage system for each of the following Marks:

1. **Lateral**
2. **Cardinal**
3. **Isolated Danger**
4. **Safe Water**
5. **Special**

1. Lateral Marks

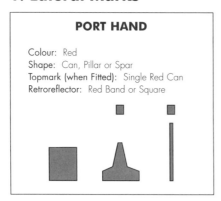

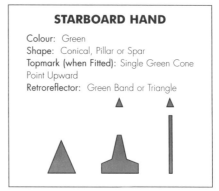

These are used to mark a well-defined channel, indicating the port and starboard sides of the route to be followed. They have to be used in conjunction with a 'Conventional Direction of Buoyage', which can either be:

a. the Local Direction of Buoyage, being the direction taken by a mariner when approaching a harbour, river, estuary, or other waterway from seaward; or

b. the General Direction of Buoyage, being the direction determined by the buoyage authorities, based wherever possible on the principle of following a clockwise direction around continents.

**DIRECTION
OF BUOYAGE**

Note that around the British Isles, the General Direction of Buoyage runs as follows:

- north along the west coast and through the Irish Sea
- east through the English Channel
- north through the North Sea

The IALA publication shows the Lateral Marks for Region A as red for port side and green for starboard side. The different shapes of buoys, colour and colour-combinations, topmarks, lights and preferred channel markers must all be learned.

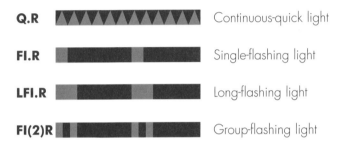

Q.R — Continuous-quick light

Fl.R — Single-flashing light

LFl.R — Long-flashing light

Fl(2)R — Group-flashing light

Red lights (shown above) as well as green lights must be learned

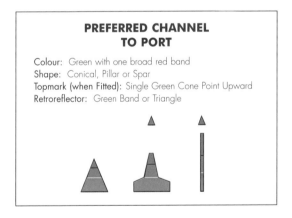

PREFERRED CHANNEL TO PORT

Colour: Green with one broad red band
Shape: Conical, Pillar or Spar
Topmark (when Fitted): Single Green Cone Point Upward
Retroreflector: Green Band or Triangle

Preferred channel to port buoys (shown above) must be learned as well as preferred channel to starboard. Refer to the IALA Maritime Buoyage System.

2. Cardinal Marks

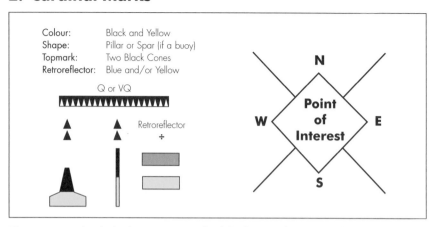

These are used to help the sea-goer to find the best (safest) navigable waters. They are placed within 1 of 4 quadrants (north, south, east or west) from the point which is being marked. It is safe to pass to the north of a north mark, south of a south mark, etc.

These marks are clearly distinguishable by their colours and topmarks, which must be memorised. Equally, the bands of colour, lights and reflectors are important.

3. Isolated Danger Marks

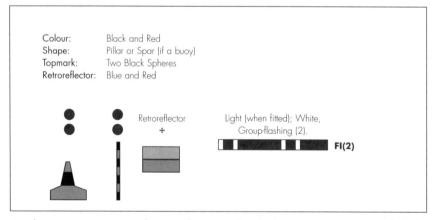

As the name suggests, these indicate isolated danger points surrounded by navigable water. They are black and red in colour.

4. Safe Water Marks

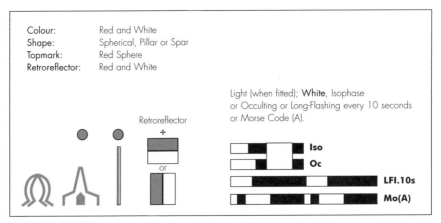

Colour: Red and White
Shape: Spherical, Pillar or Spar
Topmark: Red Sphere
Retroreflector: Red and White

Light (when fitted); **White**, Isophase or Occulting or Long-Flashing every 10 seconds or Morse Code (A).

Retroreflector ÷

Iso
Oc
LFl.10s
Mo(A)

These indicate that water is safe to navigate all around them. They are generally red and white stripes. *(It may help to remember them as 'toothpaste' coloured' - which protects you, hence they are 'safe').*

5. Special Marks

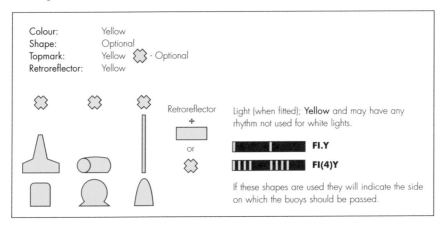

Colour: Yellow
Shape: Optional
Topmark: Yellow ✹ - Optional
Retroreflector: Yellow

Retroreflector ÷

or

Light (when fitted); **Yellow** and may have any rhythm not used for white lights.

Fl.Y
Fl(4)Y

If these shapes are used they will indicate the side on which the buoys should be passed.

These are yellow and mark some special feature to draw attention to a feature on a chart. All the above marks together with their distinguishing features must be memorised.

The IALA Maritime Buoyage System publication then goes on to give examples of how the above buoys are shown on marine charts, in the section 'Chart Symbols and Abbreviations'. These symbols and abbreviations are covered further in the publication 'Symbols and Abbreviations used on Admiralty Charts'.

Symbols and Abbreviations used on Admiralty Charts (Chart 5011)

This publication is necessary for decoding marine symbols (other than marks and buoys already discussed) since it displays and explains the symbols and abbreviations shown on marine charts.

There is a useful table of contents on the inside back cover which groups the symbols according to different categories:

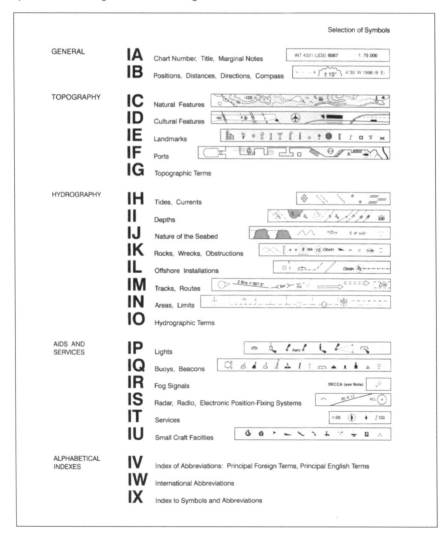

The sheer number of items may appear daunting at first glance however many of the symbols and abbreviations are self-evident, including many topographical symbols which are similar to those on Ordnance Survey maps and aviation charts.

The section on 'Aids and Services' includes buoys and beacons which have already been covered to some extent in the previous publication. Working through the sections of this publication logically, you will find that there are few symbols and abbreviations which cannot be memorised quickly and easily.

Not only is this necessary for the written exam, it might be important from a practical point of view to recognise obstruction symbols on a chart:

IK Rocks, Wrecks, Obstructions

	Plane of Reference for Depths → IH	Historic Wreck → IN		Wrecks
30	⸛20⸛ Wk	Wreck over which the exact depth is unknown, but which is considered to have a safe clearance at the depth shown		422.7
31	# ⌐Fou l¬	Remains of a wreck, or other foul area, no longer dangerous to surface navigation, but to be avoided by vessels anchoring, trawling, etc	† ◯ Foul † ⌐ Foul ㉒ Foul (Where depth known)	422.8 O17 O29a
e		Lighted wreck	⚓	K35

... whilst others might just come as a welcome relief:

Small Craft Facilities IU

20		Bottle gas		
21		Showers		
22		Laundrette	⸬	
23		Public toilets	WC	
24		Post box	▮	
25		Public telephone	⤵	i70

Tides

It is necessary to know the Definitions relating to Tides as shown in the table below:

HW	High Water	The highest level reached by the sea during a tidal oscillation
LW	Low Water	The lowest level reached by the sea during a tidal oscillation
MTL	Mean Tide Level	The level midway between Mean High Water and Mean Low Water
MSL	Mean Sea Level	The mean level of the sea at all stages of the tide
Sp	Spring Tides	Semidiurnal tides having the greatest range
Np	Neap Tides	Semidiurnal tides having the least range
MHWS	Mean High Water Springs	The average height of high water at spring tides
MHWN	Mean High Water Neaps	The average height of high water at neap tides
MHHW	Mean Higher High Water	The average height of the higher of two successive high waters under all conditions
MLHW	Mean Lower High Water	The average height of the lower of two successive high waters under all conditions
MLWS	Mean Low Water Springs	The average height of low water at spring tides
MLWN	Mean Low Water Neaps	The average height of low water at neap tides
MLLW	Mean Lower Low Water	The average height of the lower of two successive low waters under all conditions
MHLW	Mean Higher Low Water	The average height of the higher of two successive low waters under all conditions
Height of the Tide		The vertical distance measured from chart datum to the level of the sea at any instant
Flood Tide		The rising tide or ingoing tidal stream
Ebb Tide		The falling tide or outgoing tidal stream
Chart Datum		The level to which depths and drying heights are related. The level of this datum is generally coincident with the level of the lowest astronomical tide.
LAT	Lowest Astronomical Tide	The lowest tide that it is possible to predict at Standard Ports
HAT	Highest Astronomical Tide	The highest tide that it is possible to predict at Standard Ports

Photo: SkyArrow coming into land on water, with sailing boats in the background. A thorough grasp of the Colregs, Buoyage System and tidal awareness is needed for the seaplane pilot to enjoy this privilege.

The Beaufort Scale

This scale, used to estimate wind speeds and its effects, was created by Admiral Sir Francis Beaufort (1774 - 1857). He developed the scale in 1805 to help sailors estimate the winds via visual observations. The scale starts with 0 and goes up to force 12. Whilst the full list of Beaufort Scale measures is included below for completeness, notice that 'rough water' conditions start from as little as Force 3-4 and that Force 5 is considered the limit for many (even large) seaplanes.

Scale	Met Office Term	Wind Velocity Knots	Wind Velocity mph	Appearance on Water	Comments relative to Seaplanes
0	Calm	<1	<1	Surface like a mirror.	Impossible to judge height over water.
1	Light Air	1-2	1-3	Ripples with the appearance of scales are formed, but without foam crests.	Ensure competent and current on glassy water techniques before setting out in Force 0 and 1 conditions.
2	Light Breeze	3-6	4-7	Small wavelets; still short but more pronounced; crests have a glassy appearance but do not break.	Small ripples may give way to glassy water if the wind drops. Otherwise, this is 'normal' water.
3	Gentle Breeze	7-11	8-12	Large wavelets; crests begin to break. Foam has glassy appearance; perhaps some scattered whitecaps.	Normal water, approaching rough water.
4	Moderate Breeze	12-16	13-18	Small waves, becoming longer; fairly frequent whitecaps.	The limit for some small seaplanes.
5	Fresh Breeze	17-21	19-24	Moderate waves; taking on a more pronounced long form. Many whitecaps formed. Chance of some spray.	Considered 'rough water' for seaplanes and small amphibians, especially in open water.

Scale	Met Office Term	Wind Velocity Knots	Wind Velocity mph	Appearance on Water	Comments relative to Seaplanes
6	Strong Breeze	22-27	25-31	Large waves begin to form: white foam crests are more extensive everywhere. Probably some spray.	
7	Moderate Gale	28-33	32-38	Sea heaps up and white foam from breaking waves begins to be blown in streaks along the direction of the wind.	
8	Fresh Gale	34-40	39-46	Moderately high waves of greater length; edges of crests break into spindrift. The foam is blown in well-marked streaks along the direction of the wind.	
9	Severe Gale	41-47	47-54	High waves; dense streaks of foam along the direction of the wind. Sea begins to roll. Spray might affect visibility.	
10	Whole Gale/ Storm	48-54	55-63	Very high waves with long, overhanging crests. The resulting foam, in great patches, is blown in dense white streaks along the direction of the wind. On the whole, the surface of the sea takes a white appearance. The rolling of the sea becomes heavy and shock-like. Visibility is affected.	
11	Whole Gale/ Violent Storm	55-65	64-75	As force 10.	
12	Hurricane	>66	>75	The air is filled with foam and spray. Sea completely white with driving spray. Visibility very seriously affected.	

Appendix B

Knots and How to Tie Them

It is a good demonstration of seamanship if you can quickly tie an effective knot when the need arises (for example, mooring to a dock or buoy).

There are many types of knot for different situations but it is only necessary to know a few that together will cover any situation you find yourself in.

Below are a few of the most useful knots that you will need.

Bowline

This is a good versatile knot which does not slip but is easily untied. It can be used for attaching a line to a post for example.

1. Make an overhand loop with the end held toward you, then pass the end through the loop.
2. Now pass the end up behind the standing part of the line, then down through the loop again.
3. Pull the line tight.

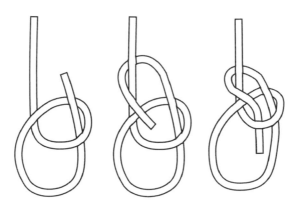

Round Turn & Two Half Hitches

This is an easily tied knot, very useful for mooring.

1. Pass the end of the rope around a post or rail.
2. Wrap the short end of the rope under and over long part of rope, pushing the end down through the loop. This is a half hitch.
3. Repeat on long rope below first half hitch and draw up tight.

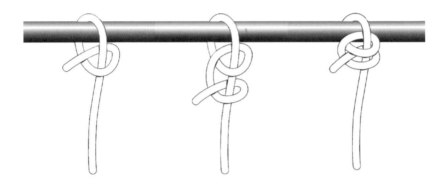

Clove Hitch

This knot is a general purpose hitch for when you need a quick, simple method of fastening a rope around a post or rail.

1. Make a turn with the rope around the object and over itself.
2. Take a second turn with the rope around the object.
3. Pull the end up under the second turn so it is between the rope and the object. Tighten by pulling on both ends.

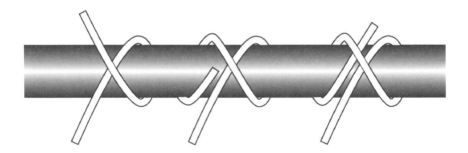

Figure Eight

This knot is ideal for attaching a line to a ring.
1. Make an underhand loop, bringing the end around and over the standing part.
2. Pass end under, and then up through the loop.
3. Draw up tight.
4. To fasten to an object, draw the bottom loop through the eye of the object (e.g. a ring or buoy)

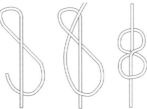

Attaching to a Mooring Cleat

Make one complete turn around a cleat or bollard, then start a figure of eight. Two or three should suffice. Make a twisted turn on the last figure of eight to secure the end.

Attaching to a Mooring Bollard

For attaching to a convenient bollard, make 'eyes' in the line and place them over the bollard threaded through each other so that they can be released in any order.

Appendix C

Bibliography and Recommended Reading List

List of Recommended Publications for the Seaplane Course:

A Small Boat Guide to the Rules of the Road by John Mellor

IALA Maritime Buoyage System (NP 735) - available from UKHO

Symbols and Abbreviations used on Admiralty Charts (Chart 5011) - available from UKHO

The Guide to Studying for the Seamanship Exam (CAA website and LASORS) includes the publications below. Note that nautical almanacs are usually available in reference libraries.

- Statutory Instrument 1996 no. 75 MERCHANT SHIPPING Safety 'The Merchant Shipping' (Distress Signals and Prevention of Collisions) Regulations 1996 - available from HMSO.
- Statutory Instrument 1990 No. 251 MERCHANT SHIPPING Safety "The Collision Regulations (Seaplanes) Order 1990 - available from HMSO.
- ICAO ANNEX 2 "Rules of the Air", Chapter 3 Paragraph 3.2.6, Water Operations.
- ICAO ANNEX 6 Parts One and Two, "Operations of Aircraft" Chapter 6, Equipment. Appendix to Chapter 6, Lights to be displayed by Aircraft.
- International Regulations for Preventing Collisions at Sea - available Royal Yachting Association.
- Reeds Nautical Almanac - Thomas Reed Publications Ltd.
- The MacMillan and Silk Cut Nautical Almanac - MacMillan Press Ltd.

Bibliography and Further Information:

Instructional Techniques for Seaplane Exercises by On-Track Aviation

Seamanship by On-Track Aviation

How to Fly Floats by J J Frey

Water Flying Concepts by Dale De Remer

Notes of a Seaplane Instructor by Burke Mees

Fly a Seaplane by Gordon K Newstrom

Flying a Floatplane by C Marin Faure

Seaplane Operations by Dale De Remer and Cesare Baj

The above and other seaplane books are available from www.lakeandair.com; www.ontrackaviation.com and the Seaplane Pilots Association (SPA) www.seaplanes.org

Step up to Floats by John M. Rennie
(available from Jack Brown's Seaplane Base, Florida)

LASORS published by the CAA

There is also a UK seaplane association:
www.seaplaneassociation.org

Notes

Notes